SCIENCE, NUMBERS, AND I

ESSAYS ON SCIENCE
by Isaac Asimov

SCIENCE, NUMBERS, AND I

BY ISAAC ASIMOV

Doubleday & Company, Inc., 1968, Garden City, New York

All essays in this volume are reprinted from *The Magazine of Fantasy and Science Fiction*. Individual essays appeared in the following issues:

Balancing the Books	July 1966
BB or Not BB, That Is the Question	August 1966
I'm Looking Over a Four-Leaf Clover	September 1966
Portrait of the Writer as a Boy	October 1966
Old Man River	November 1966
The Symbol-Minded Chemist	December 1966
Right Beneath Your Feet	January 1967
Impossible, That's All!	February 1967
Crowded!	March 1967
A Matter of Scale	April 1967
The Times of Our Lives	May 1967
Non-Time Travel	June 1967
Twelve Point Three Six Nine	July 1967
Kaleidoscope in the Sky	August 1967
The Great Borning	September 1967
Music to My Ears	October 1967
Knock Plastic!	November 1967

Library of Congress Catalog Card Number 68–14207

Printed in the United States of America

To David Asimov,
my strong-willed son

CONTENTS

INTRODUCTION

There is a story about a mother who was a little perturbed because her kindergarten-age son kept bringing home crayon pictures all in black. The sun was black, the house was black, the flowers were black.

She asked cautiously, "Do all the children draw pictures in black?"

"No," he answered indifferently, "the others draw them in different colors."

The mother took her problem to assorted neighbors who, one and all, shook their heads. It was a sign of fearful depression, of self-negation, of rejection, of autism. The mother grew more and more depressed.

Finally in utter desperation she asked her boy, "But *why* do you paint in black?"

Her son replied, "Because my desk is farthest from the crayon drawer and by the time I get there, only black crayons are left."

Moral: Ask! The answer may be simpler than your theories.

I say this because it is borne in upon me every now and then that several aspects concerning these books of essays puzzle readers, who then proceed to make up terribly ingenious theories to explain them.

This is my sixth book of science essays taken from *The Magazine of Fantasy and Science Fiction* and published by Doubleday,* and in each of these six I have exactly seventeen essays. The question therefore arises—why seventeen?

Some have speculated that it is a prime number. Some that it has some mystical or symbolic value to me. Perhaps something wonderful or horrible happened to me when I was seventeen, or perhaps I am memorializing the fact that Gauss's discovery of a method of constructing an equilateral seventeen-sided figure was of monumental importance in mathematical history.

Well, I feel my readers know me well enough (and are comfortable enough with me) to ask me directly, and here's my answer:

Back in 1949, when I set about writing my very first novel, *Pebble in the Sky*, I asked my editor, Walter I. Bradbury, how long to make it.

He said, "Make it seventy thousand words."

So I did. Ever since, I have considered 70,000 words as, somehow, the ideal length of a book. I have written much shorter books (2000 words) and much longer ones (400,000 words) but 70,000 words remain ideal in my mind.

Again, when I started writing science essays for the magazine, I asked Robert P. Mills, then its editor, how long he wanted them. He said, "Oh, about four thousand words."

So I did that too, and that remains the ideal length in my mind for essays.

Well, then, when I collect my essays into a book, I ask myself: How many 4000-word essays will fit into a 70,000-word book? And I answer myself: Seventeen.

This number of essays falls just short of the ideal 70,000 words, actually, so I add a short introduction like this one.

That's all.

* The first five are:
Fact and Fancy, 1962
View From a Height, 1963
Adding a Dimension, 1964
Of Time and Space and Other Things, 1965
From Earth to Heaven, 1966

There are also people who try to work out the principles that guide me in the selection of topics for my essays. The number that have now appeared in my six Doubleday collections is 6×17 or 102, so there is an ample field for anyone to work out those principles.

But why bother? Here are the facts of the matter as far as I am consciously aware of them. (Since I have never been psychoanalyzed, I don't know what lies hidden in my unconscious—and, come to think of it, I don't really care.)

From the moment that the magazine asked me to write a monthly essay, its editors have never either suggested a topic or quarreled with one that I chose. It has been perfectly clear to me that I have a completely free hand.

Furthermore, the editors at Doubleday have never objected to my choice of seventeen for a particular collection, or the order in which I arranged them. Again, I had a completely free hand.

So I ask you, what does a writer do when he is so fortunate as to have a completely free hand to write about anything he chooses in any way he chooses? If he is sane at all, he writes about whatever happens to interest him at the moment; and that is exactly what I do. There is no pattern less haphazard than that.

Mostly I write about various aspects of science, because that interests me a good deal.

What interests me even more than science in itself, however, are numbers and patterns. There again we might work up all sorts of weird theories, but I would like to suggest that this arises rather simply and straightforwardly from the fact that: 1) I have a neat and symmetrical mind and enjoy fitting numbers of all sorts into patterns, and 2) I like to keep myself occupied, and pattern-making never palls.

Consequently I often deal with numbers and patterns in these essays even when the subject matter is not strictly science. This book contains chapters, therefore, not only on astronomy, but on geographical statistics. There is not only a chapter on geology, but also one on musical patterns.

Then, finally, as those who read my writing can easily guess, I am interested in myself. This may seem faintly disreputable to all of you, but I can't seem to help it. No matter how I try, I find that I creep into the introduction of each essay I write.

Consequently, when I found the October 1966 issue of *The Magazine of Fantasy and Science Fiction* was to be devoted entirely to me, I proceeded to succumb to the temptation of writing an essay for that special issue that was not about either science or numbers but was entirely about myself.

And I am compounding the offense by including that essay in this book as the seventeenth and climactic one, thus justifying the title of the collection.

SCIENCE, NUMBERS, AND I

PART I

SCIENCE

1. BALANCING THE BOOKS

In my youth, my father had a candy store which remained open until 1 A.M. By then, we were naturally anxious to get the paterfamilias into the house because the store had to be open again at 6 A.M. Consequently it always irritated me to see him linger over the final chores—washing the glasses, polishing the counter, setting up the cigarette display for the next morning, and so on.

Most of all, it bothered me to watch him bend lovingly over the account books, balancing receipts versus expenditures and comparing the results with the amount recorded by the cash register.

Heaven help us all if he ended up without an even accounting. A look of anguish would cross his face and he would start recounting, re-adding, and re-shuffling the various notes he had made during the day.

You can imagine my annoyance when, after I had grown up and had returned for a short visit, I found him still engaged in this same old rigmarole. I waited for him impatiently, then said, "What's the *matter*, Pa?"

He mumbled, "I'm missing a dollar."

By that time, I had my own sources, so I reached into my pocket and said, "Here, Pa, here's a *five*-dollar bill. Take it and close the store."

But he pushed my arm to one side haughtily and said in measured, sepulchral tones, "*The books gotta balance!*" And he stayed till they did.

Later, as my knowledge of physics grew, I discovered that my father had something there. I became more and more aware of the wild gyrations physicists would go through; the theories they would evolve and smash down and re-evolve; the concepts they would create out of whole cloth; the crises they would confront—all because they believed with all their heart and soul, like my father, *that the books gotta balance!*

Take, for instance, the case of electric charge. If you have a closed system (one which is completely isolated and does not interact with the universe outside) and start with a certain amount of charge, then you must end with that precise amount of charge no matter what changes take place within the system. You cannot create electric charge out of nothing and you cannot destroy electric charge into nothing. This is called the "law of conservation of electric charge."

To be sure, there are two kinds of electric charge, which are opposed to each other and are differentiated as "positive" and "negative" (just as, in bookkeeping, we have positive money and negative money—assets and debits).

If part of a closed system contains a positive electric charge, and another part contains a negative electric charge of the same size, the two may cancel, leaving all parts of the system uncharged. The law of conservation of electric charge is not considered to be broken in this way. One merely decides to apply the law to *net* charge. If part of a closed system contains a +5 electric charge and another part contains a −3 electric charge, then the net electric charge of the system as a whole is +2 and that can neither increase nor decrease no matter what happens within that system. The system may so change as to have an electric charge of +17 in one place, +6 in another, −5 in a third, and −16 in a fourth, but $(+17)+(+6)+(-5)+(-16)=+2$. The net charge remains unchanged.

Through the nineteenth century, electric charge was dealt with only in gross amounts. In the 1890s, however, it was discovered that the atom was made up of tiny particles that carried electric charges. These came in two varieties: a proton, which carried a positive electric charge and an electron which carried a negative electric charge. The size of the electric charge was precisely the same on all protons, and on all electrons; and the size of the charge on each of the two types of particles was, except for the difference in sign, again precisely the same.

For convenience then, we can arbitrarily set the charge on the proton equal to +1, and the charge on the electron equal to −1.

Once this was discovered, electric charges in gross systems could be looked upon in subatomic terms. If a particular portion of a system had a charge of +5, that portion contained five more protons than it did electrons; if another portion had a charge of −3, that portion contained three more electrons than it did protons. Over the entire system, there were two more protons than electrons and a net charge, therefore, of +2.

In order to increase this net charge, one would have to destroy electrons or create protons; in order to decrease it, one would have to create electrons or destroy protons. Through the 1920s, it seemed quite likely that protons and electrons could not be created or destroyed under any circumstances and that seemed to explain the law of conservation of electric charge.

Indeed, one might even neglect the restriction to net electric charge, since (it seemed in the 1920s) positive charges and negative charges couldn't really cancel on the subatomic scale. A positive charge of +5 and a negative charge of −5 canceled on the gross scale when the protons and electrons mixed evenly together. Nevertheless, those protons and electrons maintained their separate existences. All the plus charges were still there and all the minus charges were still there. They merely balanced.

Then came a thunderbolt. In 1932, a particle just like the electron, but opposite in charge, was discovered by the American physicist Carl David Anderson. It was a "positive electron" or, compacting the phrase, a "positron."

It was soon discovered that if a positron encountered an electron (which it usually did within a millionth of a second after detection) there was a true cancellation of charge. The charge of both the positron and the electron disappeared, and with it the particles themselves. This process is called "annihilation."

To be sure, the positron and electron also had associated with themselves a certain amount of mass, which is an extremely compact form of energy. This mass does not undergo annihilation because we observe no such thing as positive mass and negative mass. There seems to be just one kind of mass, and the electron and positron each have an equal amount of it. When the two particles interact, the doubled mass must change into another kind of energy, and it does. It becomes radiant energy of a type known as "gamma rays." These gamma rays can be considered as being made up of particles called photons, which carry no electric charge. Two such photons can be produced in an electron/positron annihilation, so that we might say:

$$\text{electron}(-1)+\text{positron}(+1)\rightarrow\text{photon}(0)+\text{photon}(0)$$

As you see, we're back to *net* electric charge being conserved. On the left side of the arrow, the net charge is $(-1)+(+1)$, which is 0, and on the right side it is $0+0$, which is also 0. Since $0=0$, net electric charge is conserved.

But if a positron undergoes annihilation with an electron within a millionth of a second of detection, how did it come to be hanging around long enough to be detected in the first place?

It wasn't hanging around; it was created on the spot. One method of creation is indicated if we merely turn around the equation given above:

$$\text{photon}(0)+\text{photon}(0)\rightarrow\text{electron}(-1)+\text{positron}(+1)$$

Again, net electric charge is 0 on both sides of the arrow so that it is conserved. (All particle interactions, if written properly in the first place, can be reversed without losing validity. To indicate that, I will use two arrows, oppositely directed.)

Notice that just as the electron and positron must undergo *mutual* annihilation to form energy, so they must undergo *mutual* creation out of energy. You cannot form an electron alone from energy, or a positron alone. In order to form an electron alone, a net charge of −1 must be created out of nowhere; in order to form a positron alone, a net charge of +1 must be created out of nowhere. Neither is possible; *the books gotta balance!* To form both an electron *and* a positron out of uncharged photons, a net charge of 0 is produced out of 0 and that is all right. In fact, so understood is it, that an electron and positron are simultaneously formed from energy, that the process is most commonly called "pair-formation."

But now let's ask another question.

If a negatively charged electron and a positively charged positron can combine to undergo annihilation in a blaze of photons, why cannot a positively charged proton substitute for the positron? The positive charge on the proton is, as far as we know, exactly the same in nature and quantity as the positive charge on the positron, and is every bit as precisely the opposite of the charge on the electron.

Why, then, don't protons and electrons undergo mutual annihilation? Of course, it is a good thing they don't, or matter (which is made up very largely of protons and electrons in close association) would not exist. Still, why don't they?

One suspicious circumstance is that the positron matches the electron exactly in mass (and in every other way but electric charge), while the proton is much more massive than either the positron or the electron. It is 1836.11 times as massive, to be exact.

Well, then, if two particles are to undergo mutual annihilation, we might suppose that they ought to be not only opposite in sign of electric charge, but identical in all other respects, specifically in mass. Let us, then, distinguish between a light particle such as an electron and a comparatively massive one such as a proton. The electron and other light particles we can call "leptons" from a Greek word meaning small or weak. The protons and other massive particles we can call "baryons" from a Greek word meaning heavy.

The proton is not the only baryon. A particle almost identical in mass but carrying no electric charge was discovered in 1932 and named the "neutron." It too is a baryon.

Similarly, a particle even lighter than the electron and carrying no electric charge was predicted in 1930 and finally detected in 1956. It is the "neutrino" and it too is a lepton.

And where does the positron fit in? It must be a lepton since it is exactly like the electron except for the fact that it is opposite in charge. To emphasize this, the positron can be called an "antielectron" where the prefix "anti-" means opposite. I will use this name from now on, even though the older, less logical name of positron is far too firmly embedded in the scientific literature to be budged.

Similarly, one can conceive that the other particles have their opposites too. (This was first suggested in 1930 by the English physicist Paul Adrien Maurice Dirac, even before a single such opposite had actually been detected—but eventually, over the next generation, all were.) Matching the proton, therefore, is the "antiproton" which is just like the proton except that it is opposite in the nature of its electrical charge, that being -1 compared to the proton's $+1$.

Even the neutron has its opposite. One might ask, of course, how a particle can be the opposite of a neutron when the neutron has no charge to reverse.

True! Nevertheless, the neutron, despite having no overall charge, manages to possess a magnetic field, oriented in a particular direction. In the "antineutron," also uncharged, the magnetic field is oriented in the opposite direction. Similarly, in opposition to the neutrino, there is an "antineutrino."

In summary, then, see Table 1:

TABLE 1: LEPTONS AND BARYONS

Leptons		*Baryons*	
neutrino	antineutrino	proton	antiproton
electron	antielectron	neutron	antineutron

The antineutrino and antielectron can be lumped together as "antileptons" and the antiproton and antineutron can be considered "antibaryons." The antileptons and antibaryons, taken together, are "antiparticles."

Physicists have found that, in all the particle interactions they have observed, they can balance their books if they give each particle a "lepton number" or a "baryon number." Thus, the neutrino and electron each get a lepton number of +1, and the antineutrino and antielectron each get a lepton number of −1. All four have a baryon number of 0.

Similarly, the proton and neutron get a baryon number of +1 while the antiproton and antineutron get a baryon number of −1. And all four of these have a lepton number of 0.

Consider again, then, the interaction involving electron/antielectron annihilation (or, in the other direction, pair-formation).

$$\text{electron} + \text{antielectron} \rightleftharpoons \text{photon} + \text{photon}$$

On the left side of the equation, you are adding a lepton number of +1 (electron) to a lepton number of −1 (antielectron) for a total lepton number of 0. The two photons must therefore have a total lepton number of 0 also if the lepton number concept is to remain consistent, and the only way for identical photons to have a total lepton number of 0 is for each separately to have a lepton number of 0.

Is it not possible, you might ask, that there might be an antiphoton, and that the electron/antielectron annihilation might give rise to a photon and antiphoton with lepton numbers of +1 and −1 respectively? After all $(+1)+(-1)=0$ also.

The answer to that is: No! In no particle interaction ever observed have physicists had to postulate the existence of an antiphoton in order to balance the books. In fact the possible existence of antiphotons would mess things up unbearably. For instance, under certain conditions the electron/antielectron annihilation can produce a single photon, or three photons. In either of these cases, a total lepton number of zero could not possibly be attained if there were both photons and antiphotons with lepton numbers of +1 and −1. A single photon of three photons would have to have a total lepton number of +1 or −1, but *never* 0.

Physicists have therefore come to the firm conclusion that there is no separate and distinct antiphoton. The photon serves as its own opposite, and has a lepton number of 0. In that case, the annihilation interaction balances the books. The total lepton number of the electron plus antielectron is 0 and the total lepton number of the photons produced, where one, two, three, or any quantity in number, is also 0.

A similar argument can be used in the case of proton/antiproton annihilation:

$$\text{proton} + \text{antiproton} \rightleftarrows \text{photon} + \text{photon}$$

The total baryon number of the proton (+1) plus the antiproton (−1) is clearly 0, and the total baryon number of the photons produced, whatever their number, must be 0 also. Consequently, the photon must have a baryon number of 0.

Lepton numbers and baryon numbers balance in all particle interactions observed so that physicists speak of a "law of conservation of lepton number" and a "law of conservation of baryon number."

That explains why an electron and proton do not undergo mutual annihilation and why the existence of matter is possible at all. Imagine that an electron and proton combine to form photons. The electron and proton combined have a lepton number of +1 and a baryon number of +1. The photons produced can only have a total lepton number of 0 and a total baryon number of 0. Neither lepton number nor baryon number would be conserved and the reaction is therefore not observed to happen.

The photon is not unique in being neither a lepton nor a baryon. There are particles that are more massive than leptons and less massive than baryons and which are therefore called "mesons" from the Greek word for intermediate. As a specific example consider the "pion" which carries a unit positive charge and the "antipion" which carries a unit negative charge but is otherwise identical with the pion.

Both pion and antipion have a lepton number of 0 and a baryon number of 0. Nor is there any conservation law involving pions, or mesons generally. Pions, like photons, can be destroyed or created freely. (The energy represented by the photons and pions cannot be destroyed or created, of course, since the "law of conservation of energy" remains *the* most fundamental law of physics, but in this article we are talking about particles as particles and not as energy-packets.)

In Table 2, the different particles are listed in order of increasing mass with their electric charge, lepton number, and baryon number:

TABLE 2: CHARACTERIZING THE PARTICLES

	Electric Charge	*Lepton Number*	*Baryon Number*
Photon	0	0	0
Neutrino	0	+1	0
Antineutrino	0	−1	0
Electron	−1	+1	0
Antielectron	+1	−1	0
Pion	+1	0	0
Antipion	−1	0	0
Proton	+1	0	+1
Antiproton	−1	0	−1
Neutron	0	0	+1
Antineutron	0	0	−1

Notice that no two combinations in Table 2 are alike. It is therefore possible to substitute for the name of each particle, the equivalent combination value. To simplify this, since the positive and negative numbers are always units, we can omit the 1 and use only a (+) and a (−).

This gives us Table 3:

TABLE 3: COMBINATION VALUES

Photon	(ooo)
Neutrino	(o+o)
Antineutrino	(o—o)
Electron	(—+o)
Antielectron	(+—o)
Pion	(+oo)
Antipion	(—oo)
Proton	(+o+)
Antiproton	(—o—)
Neutron	(oo+)
Antineutron	(oo—)

The particles listed in Tables 2 and 3 are by no means the only ones known to exist. There are many others, most of which share one or another of the combination values shown in Table 3. For instance there is the muon which, like the electron, is (—+o) and the antimuon which, like the antielectron, is (+—o). However, the muon and antimuon differ from the electron and antielectron in mass.*

Again, there is the neutral pion which, like the photon, is (ooo). The neutral pion differs from the photon both in mass and in a quantity called "spin."

Yet again, there is the lambda particle which, like the neutron, is (oo+) but which differs from the neutron in mass and in quantities called "strangeness" and "isotopic spin."

Some of these other properties are conserved (notably spin and strangeness) and if they and others were added to Table 2, more extensive combination values could be drawn up which would distinguish all the particles from each other.

* The muon and antimuon are also leptons. Indeed the law of conservation of lepton number can be divided into two parts, "the law of conservation of electron family number" and "the law of conservation of muon family number." Each part holds separately and the two add together to keep the law of conservation of lepton number generally valid. However, this refinement doesn't concern us here.

The only exception to this is the strange case of the muon-neutrino and the muon-antineutrino. These have combinations of (0+0) and (0—0) respectively, like the ordinary neutrino and antineutrino. Nor do the two kinds of neutrinos differ in any other known property, whether mass, spin, strangeness, or what have you. Although the two sets of neutrinos behave like distinctly different particles, no one yet knows in what physical property they are different.

In this article, I am restricting myself only to the particles mentioned in Tables 2 and 3 and for them the three-item combination values are sufficient. Each of the eleven particles has its distinct combination and these can be substituted for the names of the particles in describing interactions. The virtue of doing so lies in the fact that one can then tell at a glance whether the laws of conservation of electric charge, lepton number, and baryon number are being conserved or not. (I must warn the Gentle Reader that the idea of doing this is, as far as I know, original with me, and lacks the cachet of orthodox scientific approval. However, I'm going to do it, anyway.)

For instance, in the electron/antielectron annihilation (or pair-formation) process, we can write:

$$(-+0)+(+-0)=(000)+(000)$$

Arithmetically, the number of photons produced does not matter. They can vary in number as conditions change but any number of (000)'s add up to (000). Let us simplify matters, then, by never writing more than one photon. The equation therefore becomes:

$$(-+0)+(+-0)=(000)$$

In adding combination values, all we have to remember is that (+) and (—) stand for +1 and —1 respectively and must be treated accordingly, so that, as an example (+)+(—) =0.

In that case, the combination values of electron and positron add up as follows:

$$\begin{array}{r} (-+\text{o}) \\ +\ (+-\text{o}) \\ \hline (\text{o}\ \text{o}\ \text{o}) \end{array}$$

Since this means that (ooo)=(ooo), which is certainly so, the various laws of conservation are observed in the electron/anti-electron interaction. You can demonstrate the same thing for any annihilation or pair-formation process.

On the other hand, the interaction of a proton and an electron would be (+o+)+(−+o). This would add up not to (ooo) as would be required in annihilation but to (o++), a combination value that, as far as we know, is non-existent. Result: no proton/electron annihilation. Descartes might say: "(+o+)+(−+o) is not equal to (ooo); therefore I am."

But there are interactions that do happen and yet are not annihilations. To take one of the best known of these, consider the spontaneous breakdown of a neutron. An isolated neutron was found, in 1950, to change into a proton and an electron. If that were all, we would have something like: (oo+)→(+o+)+(−+o). But this doesn't balance, for if we add (+o+) and (−+o), we get (o++) instead of the (oo+) we started with.

To get rid of that unwanted (+) in the middle, we must add the combination (o−o) which, as you can see in Table 3, is the antineutrino. (It is this requirement of an antineutrino or, in some cases, a neutrino, to save various conservation laws, that forced physicists to accept the existence of neutrinos and antineutrinos long before they were actually detected.)

Furthermore, the neutron, in its breakdown, liberates energy, which means that it forms a photon or photons, too. We will take one photon into account and say that a neutron breaks down to form a proton, an electron, an antineutrino, and a photon and represent that thus:

$$(\text{oo}+)\rightleftarrows(+\text{o}+)+(-+\text{o})+(\text{o}-\text{o})+(\text{ooo}).$$

If we add all the combination values on the right side, we have:

$$\begin{array}{rc} & (+\circ+) \\ & (-+\circ) \\ & (\circ-\circ) \\ + & (\circ\circ\circ) \\ \hline & (\circ\circ+) \end{array}$$

Thus, we end up with $(\circ\circ+)=(\circ\circ+)$ and the conservation laws are upheld.

Again, within the atomic nucleus, the various particles are held together because pions interact with the protons and neutrons of the nucleus. This can be represented as:

$$(\circ\circ+)+(+\circ\circ)\rightleftarrows(+\circ+)$$

This is the combination-value way of saying that a neutron plus a pion equals a proton and the fact that we end with $(+\circ+)=(+\circ+)$ shows that the conservation laws are upheld.

Where does all this take us? Well, my father acted as though the fate of the Universe depended on his balancing his books and so do the physicists. The conservation laws take us, with an easy leap, from the realm of the infinitesimally small to the realm of the infinitely large; for the theories of the structure, origin, and fate of the universe depend, in part, on the manner in which the small (+)'s and (—)'s of this article add up. We shall see why in the following chapters.

2. BB OR NOT BB, THAT IS THE QUESTION

All scientists have fun* but the ones that have the most fun are, in my own opinion, the cosmogonists. ("Cosmogony" is from Greek words meaning "universe-birth" so cosmogonists are obviously involved in the study of the origin and development of the Universe.)

Nobody was around at the origin, so there are no eyewitness reports. Cosmogonists can reach their conclusions only on the basis of some very subtle observations that are just barely within reach of modern instruments. This gives them vast scope within which to exercise their imaginations and a vast background—all of space and time—against which to exercise it. Who could resist?

No astronomer and hardly any non-astronomers. Certainly not I.

If I am held back at all, it is that the task of working up a good cosmogony, a *good* one, requires a far greater knowledge of mathematics and of theoretical physics than I possess. However, while that inhibits me, it doesn't stop me cold. I have my opinions on the subject and if I were to try to bottle them up forever, the internal pressure might do damage to the speculative centers of my cerebrum. So, before returning to the immediate concerns of the previous chapter, here goes.

There are a number of Universe models which describe, in the most general terms, the manner in which our Universe came to

* In their work, I mean. What they do outside business hours is their own concern, and I wouldn't dream of inquiring.

be organized into the fashion we now find it, and which predict how it may be expected to change further (or not change further) as we progress into the future.

All the models have to fit one great overall observation. The most distant objects we can see, the galaxies outside our own local cluster, all show a "red shift." That is, the characteristic lines present in their spectra are displaced toward the red end of the spectrum in every case.

The usual interpretation of this red shift is to the effect that the galaxies are receding from us. A receding object is known to show a red shift in the light it sends us; and the greater the velocity of recession the greater the extent of the red shift.

It so happens that the farther the galaxy (judging from its brightness and from some other considerations) the greater the red shift, and this is what would be expected if the Universe as a whole were expanding. This picture of an expanding Universe is a convenient one, for it fits the equations worked out by Albert Einstein in his General Theory of Relativity. Nor could anyone suppose that Einstein had arranged his theory to allow for the expansion, for he announced it in 1916 without suspecting the existence of expansion; and the observational data that enforced acceptance of an expanding Universe became clear only in the 1920s.

Any Universe model must, therefore, take the expansion of the Universe into account and explain it in physical terms if possible. If a Universe model involves a non-expanding Universe, then some alternate explanation that will hold water must be found for the red shift.

On the whole, the Universe models may be put into two classes: 1) continuous creation, and 2) big bang. We can refer to them, conveniently, by their neatly alliterative initials, CC and BB.

According to the CC models, creation is continuing all the time, single atom by single atom, but so very slowly that no instruments in the armory of science could conceivably detect it now. Still, in the course of some billions of years, the amount of matter in the Universe would double as a result of this slow drizzle of creation.

However, the Universe is expanding and in those same billions of years, the galaxies would have moved apart to the point where the amount of space between them had doubled. Most of the new matter would form, on a purely random basis, in the vast spaces between the galaxies. There they would collect into new galaxies, so that the distance between adjacent galaxies would remain the same in the long run. Nor would there seem to be twice as many galaxies altogether because in the course of the expansion of the Universe, the more distant galaxies would be carried so far away that their red shifts would become so extreme as to allow little or no light to reach us at all.

By the CC model, then, galaxies are being continually pushed beyond the detectable horizon, while new galaxies are continually being formed, so that the overall order of the Universe does not change with time. There is no true beginning of the Universe, no true ending. The Universe is eternal and—in the large view—unchanging. Individual galaxies, such as our own, would change, to be sure. They would be collected from the gathering matter between galaxies, form stars, evolve, and, eventually, die; but the system of galaxies would remain unchanged.

According to the BB models, however, this is not so. The Universe has both a beginning and an ending; or at least there was a time long ago when it was radically different from what it is now and there will be a time in the future when it will be radically different again.

In the BB models, the expansion of the Universe is explained in a directly physical manner. If the Universe is expanding as though it were being blown apart, that is because something once did blow it apart.

Once long ago, all the matter of the Universe was crushed together into an incredibly concentrated mass. This "cosmic egg" exploded and out of its remnants were formed the galaxies, which are still flying apart against the pull of mutual gravitational attraction in response to the force of that tremendous long-ago explosion.

Which is it, then, CC or BB? Continuous creation or big bang?

The Universe as it exists today is consistent with either type of model, but this is not so of the Universe as it exists all through time.

By the CC model, there is *no* overall change with time. Old galaxies recede and new ones form in such a way that galaxies are strewn through space with the same thickness now, and a trillion years in the past, and a trillion years in the future. Furthermore, the new galaxies mix with the old ones in purely random fashion, so that at any point in time, any given galaxy will be surrounded by galaxies in all stages of development from the very new to the very old.

By the BB model, there *is* an overall change with time. Billions of years ago, all the galaxies were crowded together and all were young. Billions of years from now, all the galaxies will be spread widely apart and all will be old. Furthermore, at any given moment of time, any particular galaxy will be surrounded by others of like age.

This means that we can distinguish between the CC and BB models by building a time machine, traveling into the far past or far future and taking a quick look at the Universe.

And we can do that—after a fashion. Light cannot travel faster than 186,282 miles per second. This is fast on the terrestrial scale but it is a mere creep in the cosmos as a whole. Light from the more distant galaxies takes a billion years or more to reach us. This means that what we see when we look at the very distant galaxies is the Universe as it was billions of years ago.

All we have to decide, then, is whether what we see far, far away is essentially the same as what we see in our own neighborhood. If it *is,* then the BB model is eliminated; if it is *not,* then the CC model is eliminated. (Notice that I only mention the eliminated; I don't say that anything is established. To eliminate the BB-model does *not* establish the CC model for it is not an either-or proposition. *Both* models may be wrong. Similarly, to eliminate the CC model does not, of itself, establish the BB. Nevertheless, elimination is a great step forward; at least there is one wrong road we need explore no further.)

Of course, there is a catch. It is very difficult to see things beyond the billion-light-year mark. Small differences between there and here are bound to escape our notice if only because we can't possibly see the very distant galaxies in any detail. If there is a difference at all, we can only hope that it is a great, big difference that shows up very clearly even across billions of light years of space.

Astronomers could scarcely believe their luck when exactly that happened.

It seems that certain stars which had appeared to be dim and undistinguished members of our own Galaxy suddenly gained notoriety at the very end of the 1950s by turning out to be sources of radio waves.

Now there are lots of radio-wave sources in the Universe, but only one of them had appeared to be an ordinary star. That one exception is our own Sun and we detect its radio-wave radiation only because it is so close to us. If it were merely as far off as the nearest star, its radio-wave radiation would become indetectable. The radio waves we do detect from beyond the Solar system come from remnants of supernovas, or (if outside our Galaxy altogether) from unusual catastrophes such as exploding galaxies.

Here, however, were radio sources that seemed to be ordinary stars of our own Galaxy.

Astronomers turned their full attention to these stars and found faint little wisps of nebulosity attached to some of them, so it began to look as though they might be stars, but not ordinary ones. Secondly, their spectra showed lines that could not be identified and were not like those of any other object. They might be stars but, far from being ordinary, they began to seem most extraordinary.

Then, in early 1963, it was noticed that some of the lines had the spacing of certain hydrogen lines, except that those hydrogen lines ought to be in the ultraviolet. Could the lines have shifted redward into the visible region? That would be a red shift with a vengeance. Other lines became familiar too, if that same red shift were allowed. But if such a red shift were allowed and the stars were assumed to possess them because they were participating in the general expansion of the Universe, they would have to be far off indeed. To be at the place where general expansion was carrying them away from us at *that* rate, they would have to be at perfectly enormous distances—over a billion light years away.

If that were so, the stars could not be stars at all, ordinary or extraordinary, for nothing the size of a star could be seen at such distances. They were "quasi-stellar" (that is, "star-like") radio sources. In no time, the ugly term "quasi-stellar" was shortened to the even uglier "quasar."

By now, over a hundred suspected quasars have been discovered and several dozen have had their spectra studied in detail. All have enormous red shifts. The quasars all seem to be beyond the billion-light-year mark and a couple have been placed at a distance of possibly eight billion light years. (These are the farthest objects known.)

For quasars to appear as bright as they do, even though at such enormous distances, they must be luminous indeed. The average quasar must be some hundred times as luminous as the average Galaxy. And yet they are not a hundred times as large as the average Galaxy. If they were, they would have visible shapes instead of being mere points of light—even at their huge distances. In fact, astronomers have reason to suspect the quasars to be no more than a very few light years in diameter (compared to our own Galaxy's 100,000-light-year span).

Astronomers are driving themselves to distraction these days trying to figure out how an object can be only a few light years across yet shine with the fury of a hundred galaxies. What is the source of the energy? How is it tapped? What starts a quasar? What ends it?

This sort of worry we can put to one side for the moment.

Regardless of what makes a quasar tick, let us simply concentrate on the fact that it exists and that it is radically different from anything in our own neighborhood.

Assuming that the quasars are really very distant—billions of light years away—then the light we see them by left them billions of years ago, and those quasars inhabit a Universe billions of years younger than our own. Also, there are no quasars near us.

It follows, then, that billions of years ago there existed a Universe relatively rich in quasars, whatever they are; and now we live in a Universe that has no quasars. The logical conclusion is that there is a broad and marked distinction between the past and the present; that the quasars represent short-lived objects that could exist only in a young Universe. It is not necessary to know what the quasars are in detail to see that this eliminates the CC models which insist on a Universe that is unchanging in its broad aspects.

We are then left with the BB models which may be wrong also —but which may be right.

But wait, not so fast. All this depends on the quasars really being located at billion-plus light-year distances. What says they are? Only the red shift? Well, perhaps the red shift has some other explanation and the quasars are, after all, exactly what they appear to be—dim stars of our own Galaxy.

Ah, but the red shift isn't quite all. One of the quasars (the best studied one, in fact) rejoices in the name 3C273* and lies in the direction of a cluster of galaxies in the constellation Virgo. This cluster is surrounded by a cloud of hydrogen and the light from 3C273 shows spectral lines that would indicate that some of its radiation has been absorbed by hydrogen. It seems natural to suppose that the light from 3C273 has passed through the cloud surrounding the Virgo cluster on its way to us and that 3C273 must therefore lie beyond the cluster. Right?

Well, the Virgo cluster is known to be 40,000,000 light years

* Because it is the 273d object listed in the *Third Cambridge Catalogue of Radio Sources.*

away so 3C273 must be farther away than that. And 3C273 is the nearest of the known quasars. At least, it has the smallest red shift.

This seems to eliminate the chance that the quasars are really peculiar stars of our own Galaxy. Quasar 3C273 certainly isn't and if one quasar is a large, distant, super-luminous object, why should all the other objects that resemble it be small, close-by stars.

On the other hand, even if the quasars are far away, are they *very* far away? The Virgo cluster is 40 million light years away; and maybe 3C273 is only 50 million light years away. Maybe other quasars are only 10 million light years away.

If the distance of the quasars is in the millions, rather than in the billions, of light years, then they don't have to be so luminous to appear as bright as they do. They might be only as bright as 1/100 of a galaxy instead of 100 galaxies. An object 1/100 as bright as a galaxy would be far easier to explain and astronomers could breathe more freely. Furthermore, quasars that close and dim would mean that quasars probably exist at greater distances too, but then become too dim in appearance to detect. In that case, it would be reasonable to suspect that quasars are quite a common phenomenon, spread out all over the Universe with only the nearest being detectable. The Universe would then appear to show no startling differences past and present and the CC model would no longer be eliminated.

But if quasars are comparatively close to us, we are still left with an overriding problem—why the enormous red shift? As far as I know there are three causes for a red shift; two legitimate and one doubtful. Let's consider the doubtful one first.

Every once in a while someone suggests that light loses energy as it travels and gradually increases in wave length, thus shifting toward the red. The red shift then becomes evidence for what is called "tired light." According to that view, the Universe need not be expanding at all. The more distant the galaxy, the more tired the light after its long travels and the redder; that's all.

The catch to this theory is that no one has ever been able to give a good mechanism whereby such a tired-light red shift can take place. If the light loses energy, that energy must be gained by something else (according to the law of conservation of energy). What else? No one knows.

It might be that we're just not smart enough to know what is picking up the energy, or it might be that the law of conservation of energy doesn't work under all conditions after all. But then, we should be able to measure the slight tiredness of light originating from the stars of our own Galaxy—maybe even in the course of laboratory experiments—and we don't.

In short, there is no theoretical justification or observational evidence for the tired-light red shift, so let's eliminate it.

That leaves the two legitimate explanations for a red shift. One of these involves a gravitational field which, according to Einstein's General Theory of Relativity (and backed by observation), would reduce the energy of light leaving a body.

But for the red shift of the quasars to be caused by gravitation, so huge a gravitational field would be required, and, therefore, so huge and dense a mass, that astronomers would be deeply in trouble. It would be just as difficult to explain a huge, super-dense nearby quasar as a huge, super-luminous distant quasar.

In fact, I think most astronomers would prefer the problems of super-distance to those of super-gravitation any day.

That leaves us with the explanation of the red shift by rapid recession; but if so, need that recession be interpreted as part of the general expansion of the Universe? Is that the *only* possible type of recession?

Suppose the quasar were nearby, can't we have it receding at a sizable fraction of the speed of light just through some explosion on a galactic scale—a kind of "little-bang" hypothesis? Its rapid recession, misinterpreted as part of the general expansion of the Universe, might then cause astronomers to tab the object as a thousand times more distant than it really is.

In 1966, in fact, an astronomer at Stanford reported that at least five quasars seem to be suspiciously near "peculiar galaxies"

—galaxies which may have undergone some catastrophe and been left with atypical shapes.

And yet, if galactic explosions produced quasars in the shape of million-star fragments, should not some of them have been hurled in *our* general direction and not yet have passed us? Should not some of them be approaching us, rather than receding from us? Should not *one* of them be approaching?

An approaching quasar would show a huge shift of spectral lines in the opposite direction—toward the violet. And yet not one quasar, not one, has been found to possess a huge "violet-shift." Many quasars are receding rapidly; not one quasar is approaching.

Galactic explosions that hurl everything in the direction opposite us and nothing toward us are too much to ask of coincidence.

Another possibility is that the quasars are not ejected at super-velocities and are not moving very rapidly at all. They might, however, be collapsing at enormous rates. The surface of the object, which is radiating light toward us, would then be pictured as moving inward toward the center of the object and away from us. It would be this "recession" that would then be responsible for the red shift. In that case, it wouldn't matter whether the quasars were moving slowly away from us or slowly toward us; the super-rapid collapse would swallow up everything and it would always appear to be a recession and would always produce a red shift.

Yet such collapses would involve the motion of matter toward a center that could not be more than a light year or so distant, at best. At the indicated speeds of recession (large fractions of the speed of light) such collapses couldn't last more than a few months. Strange that we should catch so many bodies in the midst of such an evanescent stage of evolution. That, it seems to me, is also asking too much of coincidence.

So it's my own opinion that we are left with one explanation only of the red shift—enormous distance on the part of quasars and participation in the general expansion of the Universe. And that means that the CC models of the Universe are eliminated.

We are left with the BB models—the big bang—which may also be wrong, but which may be right.

Suppose, then, that the Universe *did* begin as a vast single mass of tremendously dense matter, and that that cosmic egg exploded. At the moment of explosion it must have been tremendously hot—one estimate, advanced in 1965, was that the initial temperature was 10 billion degrees absolute (10,000,000,000° K) or 18 billion degrees Fahrenheit.

If so, then if our instruments could penetrate far enough into the vast distances of space, they might be penetrating deeply enough into the past to catch a whiff of the radiation that accompanied the big bang. At the temperatures indicated for the initial fireball, that radiation should be in the short-wave x-ray region. However, at such distances, the red shift would be so extreme that the radiation would be pushed far, far toward and beyond the visible red into the microwave region of the electromagnetic spectrum. It would then give the kind of radiation that would be expected of an object at a temperature of merely 10° K (that is, ten degrees above absolute zero).

Early in 1966 a general background of microwave radiation was indeed detected, radiation of a type quite similar to the kind predicted, except that the distribution of wave length was equivalent to a temperature of only 3° K. This means that astronomers may have detected what might be called the birth-cry of the Universe. The unexpectedly low temperature to which the microwave radiation is equivalent leads astronomers to suspect that the initial fireball was cooler than expected and this may require some juggling which we need not go into since it would not affect the main problem—BB or not BB.

Between the quasars and the birth-cry, I am now sold on the BB models. And this isn't a glad decision for me, either, because I consider the CC model (continuous creation) much more satisfying from a purely emotional viewpoint.

If we accept a BB model, we are forced to ask an embarrassing question. This huge cosmic egg that exploded to form our Universe—where did it come from?

One way of answering that question is to shrug and say, "It always existed."

But if it always existed, why did it suddenly explode? If it existed for an eternity without exploding, what kicked it off all of a sudden?

Let's consider. Some BB models visualize a single explosion and a perpetual recession. All the clusters of galaxies would recede from each other until the distances separating them were so vast that no one cluster could be detected from any other. When that day comes, our Universe would consist of our own Galaxy, the Andromeda galaxy, and about a dozen additional small members of the Local Cluster. That's all. And by that time, the Cluster would be dying; our Sun would be a white dwarf.

This is rather disheartening to envisage, even though all of us will be safely dead long before such a denouement.

On the other hand, there is also a possibility that the initial explosion was not strong enough to hurl the galactic clusters apart indefinitely. Rather the velocity of recession is being slowly cut down by the unwearying force of mutual gravitation among the pieces of the Universe. Eventually, then, like a ball thrown upward, the exploding Universe would slow to a spent halt, and then start to fall together again, faster and faster and faster. Its matter would drive together and form the cosmic egg again, which would, of course, explode again at once and start the cycle over.

This is what is called the "oscillating universe" and it has recently been suggested that the period of oscillation from one cosmic egg to the next is a little over 80,000,000,000 years.

If this is so, then we don't have to wonder how a cosmic egg can exist for all eternity and then suddenly explode. It doesn't exist for all eternity at all. It exists only for a short period every eighty billion years; forming and exploding—forming and exploding—forming and exploding—

But the material making up the cosmic egg—the material that is now spread out into the matter and energy of the Universe as we know it—where did that come from?

Ah, now we are ready for my own cosmological theory, which I will discuss in the next chapter, using material from this chapter and the preceding one.

3. I'M LOOKING OVER A FOUR-LEAF CLOVER

History is full of apocryphal stories; stories about people saying and doing things they never really said and did—like George Washington chopping down the cherry tree, or Galileo dropping weights off the Leaning Tower of Pisa. Unfortunately, apocryphal stories are so much more interesting than the truth that it is impossible to kill them. And what's even more unfortunate for me, specifically, is that my memory is so selective that I never forget an apocryphal story, even though I frequently have trouble remembering facts.

For instance, here's a story, probably apocryphal (or I wouldn't remember it so tenaciously) about St. Augustine.

He was asked once, by a scoffer, "What did God spend His time doing before He created Heaven and Earth?"

And St. Augustine roared back, without hesitation, "Creating Hell, for those who ask questions like that!"

But I hope St. Augustine was just joshing when he said that, for having talked about the conservation laws in Chapter 1, and about the expanding Universe in Chapter 2, I want to go on to discuss my theories as to the birth and development of the Universe in the light of the conservation laws; and to do that I will (among other things) have to ask that unaskable question —what came before the beginning?

I ended Chapter 2 with the picture of an oscillating Universe; one that first expands, then contracts, then expands, then contracts, and so on over and over again, with each cycle of expansion and contraction taking some eighty billion years, and with an extremely dense "cosmic egg" at the point of maximum contraction in each cycle.

In continuing the discussion, let's begin by asking whether all the cycles are identical, or whether there is some change from cycle to cycle; perhaps a steady, one-way change.

For instance, we might argue that as the Universe expands, it radiates massless particles—photons and neutrinos—constantly. These photons and neutrinos, we can say, move outward and are forever lost. When the Universe contracts again, the mass that comes together into a cosmic egg is smaller by the loss of the mass-equivalent of the energy represented by the lost radiation. This would continue with each cycle, each cosmic egg being less massive than the one before, until finally a cosmic egg is formed that possesses so little mass that it can no longer explode properly. When that happens the entire Universe is represented by one extremely large but slowly dying mass of condensed matter.

In that case, we would be living not merely in an oscillating Universe but in a damped oscillating one. The Universe, in that view, would be like a bouncing ball that is not very elastic. Each bounce is lower than the one before and finally the ball does not bounce at all but just lies there.

That is rather a neat picture for it produces a logical end, the kind of an end we are familiar with in ordinary life and one we might therefore be disposed to accept. But suppose we look backward in time? What about the cosmic egg that existed before the one that started the present expansion? That earlier one had to be larger than ours, and the one before that had to be even larger, and the one before that still larger. To move back in time and find ever-larger cosmic eggs, exploding with ever-greater violence is troublesome, for an endlessly increasing mass may be hard to handle. The damped oscillating Universe produces a neat overall end but no neat overall beginning.

Fortunately we don't have to complicate matters by picturing such a damped oscillation. Photons and neutrinos are not "forever lost." To be sure, they move outward from their source of radiation in a "straight line" but what do we mean by a "straight line"? Suppose we draw a straight line on the surface of the Earth. It might seem to us that if we extend that line with perfect straightness, it will go on and on forever and that a point traveling along it will be "forever lost" to anyone standing at the place of origin of the line. However, you know and I know that the Earth's surface is curved and that the "straight line" will eventually (if we assume the Earth to be a perfect sphere) come back to the place of origin.

In the same way, photons and neutrinos, in traveling a "straight line" by our local-neighborhood-of-the-Universe definition, are actually traveling in a grand circle and will return, roughly speaking, to the point of origin. The Universe of "curved space" has a finite volume and all it contains, matter and energy, must remain within that volume.

As the Universe contracts, not only matter, but also photons and neutrinos must be crowded together. The massless particles are still traveling in "straight lines" but these "straight lines" curve ever more sharply; and in the end all the contents of the previous cosmic egg are brought back into another cosmic egg, with nothing lost. Each cosmic egg is precisely like the one before and the one that will come after and there is no damping. In a strictly oscillating Universe of this sort, there is neither beginning nor end, nor, *on the whole*, any change. If this faces us with the uncomfortable concept of eternity, it is at least an essentially unchanging eternity.

Within a single cycle of the oscillation, of course, there is a beginning at one cosmic egg, an end at the next, and colossal change in between.

But what is the nature of the cosmic egg? That depends on the nature of the Universe. On the subatomic scale, our portion of the Universe is made up, in the main, of six kinds of particles: protons, electrons, neutrons, photons, neutrinos, and antineutrinos. The other particles that exist are present in vanishingly small traces on the whole and may be ignored.

The subatomic particles are associated into atoms at the moment and these atoms are associated into stars and galaxies. We can assume that the six kinds of particles that make up our part of the Universe make up all of it and that even the farthest galaxy is essentially similar in fundamental makeup to our own bodies.

As all the mass and energy of the Universe crunch together into the cosmic egg, the levels of organization of the Universe break down, one by one. The galaxies and stars come together in one contracting mass. The more complicated atoms decompose into hydrogen, absorbing neutrinos and photons as they do so. The hydrogen atoms break apart into protons and electrons, absorbing photons as they do so. The protons and electrons combine to form neutrons, absorbing antineutrinos as they do so.

In the end, the Universe has been converted into a cosmic egg made up of a mass of hard-packed neutrons—a mass of "neutronium."

Well-packed neutronium would have a density of about 400,000,000,000,000 grams per cubic centimeter, so that if the mass of the Sun were packed into neutronium, it would form a sphere with a radius of about 6.6 miles.

If we consider that the mass of the Milky Way Galaxy is about 135,000,000,000 times that of the Sun, then the whole of our Galaxy, converted into neutronium, would form a sphere with a radius of about 33,600 miles.

If we consider the Universe to contain a mass, 100,000,000,000 times that of our Galaxy, then the cosmic egg would have a radius of 156,000,000 miles. If the center of such a cosmic egg were made to coincide with the center of our Sun, the surface of the cosmic egg would almost coincide with the orbit of Mars. And even if the mass of the Universe were twenty thousand times as large as the mass I have cited, the cosmic egg, if it were composed of pure, well-packed neutronium, would be no larger than the orbit of Pluto.

How does the cosmic egg fit in with the conservation laws discussed in Chapter 1?

One can easily imagine that the momentum of the cosmic egg as a whole is zero, by defining the egg as motionless. When the cosmic egg explodes and expands, the individual portions have momentum in one direction or another, but all the momenta add up to zero. In the same way, the angular momentum of the cosmic egg can be defined as zero and while the parts of the expanding universe have individual angular momenta that are not zero, the total is zero.

In short, it is tempting to try to establish a rule that for any conserved quantity, the value of that quantity in the cosmic egg is zero, or is capable of being defined as zero without logical difficulties.

Since this notion is, as far as I know, original with me—especially in the manner I intend to develop it in the course of this article—I shall throw modesty to the dogs and speak of it as "Asimov's Cosmogonic Principle."

The most economical way of expressing the principle is, "In the Beginning, there was Nothing."

For instance, how about the conservation of electric charge? Of the six particles making up the Universe, one (the proton) has a positive charge and one (the electron) has a negative charge. These cannot combine and cancel electric charge under ordinary conditions (see Chapter 1), but in forming the cosmic egg, conditions may be extreme enough to make the two combine to form neutrons. The electric charge of the cosmic egg is then zero. (In the Beginning, there was No Charge.)

In the course of the explosion and expansion of the cosmic egg, charge appears, to be sure, but in equal quantities of positive and negative so that the total remains zero.

And what about lepton number (see "Balancing the Books").

Of the six particles making up the Universe, three are leptons. The electron and the neutrino have lepton numbers of +1, while the antineutrino has a lepton number of −1. In the formation of neutrons, all three disappear, and it is not unreasonable to suppose that the manner of the disappearance is such as to cancel out the lepton number and leave the cosmic egg with a lepton number of zero.

On the whole, one can arrange matters to show that the values of all but two of the conserved quantities known to physicists are zero in the cosmic egg, or can logically be defined as zero. The two exceptions are baryon number and energy.

Let's begin with the baryon number.

Of the six particles making up the Universe, two are baryons, the proton and the neutron. Each has a baryon number of +1. Since there is no particle with a baryon number of −1 in the list of those making up the Universe, there is no chance of cancellation of baryon number, and no chance (or so it would now appear) of a cosmic egg possessing a baryon number of zero. In the process of cosmic egg formation, the protons disappear, to be sure, but for each proton that disappears, a neutron is formed and the baryon number remains positive.

Indeed, if the cosmic egg contains the mass of 100,000,000,000 galaxies the size of ours, then it is made up of 1.6×10^{79} baryons and its baryon number is +16,000,000,000,000,000,000,000,000,000,000,000,000,000,000,000,000,000,000,000,000,000,000,000,000,000,000. This is a terribly long way from zero and makes hash of Asimov's Cosmogonic Principle.

There's a way out. There are particles with negative baryon numbers, even if those do not seem to occur in any but the tiniest traces in our neck of the woods. The antineutron, for instance, has a baryon number of −1. Well, suppose that the cosmic egg does not consist of neutrons only, but of neutrons and antineutrons, half and half. The baryon number would then be zero, as the Principle requires.

The neutron half of the cosmic egg would explode to form

protons and electrons which would combine to form atoms. The antineutron half would explode to from antiprotons and anti-electrons (positrons) which would combine to form antiatoms.

In short, we have now talked ourselves into supposing that the Universe is made up of equal quantities of matter and antimatter—but is it? It is absolutely inconceivable that the Universe be made up of matter and antimatter all mixed up, for if it were, the two would interact at once to produce photons. (That's exactly what happens when we, by might and main, produce a trifling quantity of antimatter in the laboratory.) A Universe composed of equal quantities of matter and antimatter, all mixed up, would actually be composed of a mass of photons, which are neither matter nor antimatter. The cosmic egg would be nothing more than compacted photons.

But the Universe is *not* made up of photons only. If, then, it is made up of equal quantities of matter and antimatter, those must be separated—effectively separated—so that they do not interact to form photons. The only separation that is separate enough would be on the galactic scale. In other words, there may be galaxies made up of matter, and other galaxies made up of antimatter. Galaxies and antigalaxies, so to speak.

We have no way of telling, so far, whether the Universe actually contains galaxies and antigalaxies. If a galaxy and an antigalaxy met, enormous quantities of energy would be formed as matter-antimatter annihilation took place. No clear-cut case of such an event has yet been detected, though there are some suspicious cases. Secondly, galaxies produce vast quantities of neutrinos as the hydrogen atoms are built up to helium in the stars they contain; while antigalaxies produce vast quantities of antineutrinos by way of the analogous process involving antimatter. When the day comes that astronomers can detect neutrinos and antineutrinos from distant galaxies, and pinpoint their sources, the galaxies and antigalaxies may be identified.

In a Universe made up of galaxies and antigalaxies, we can picture the crunching together of the cosmic egg in a new way. Neutrons and antineutrons would be formed and these would undergo mutual annihilation to form photons. We would have "photonium" in the cosmic egg, rather than neutronium. What the properties of photonium would be like, I can't imagine.

But what causes the photonium to break up into matter and antimatter in such a way that separate galaxies of each kind can be formed? Why doesn't the photonium break up into neutrons and antineutrons so well mixed that they annihilate each other at once? In short, why isn't the photonium stable? Why doesn't it remain photonium?

Well, there are theories that an antiparticle is merely a particle that is moving backward in time. If you take a film of a positron in a magnetic field, it seems to curve, let us say, leftward, rather than rightward, as an electron would under similar conditions. However, if the film is run backward, then the positron curves rightward, like an electron.

On the subatomic scale, it makes no difference whether time moves "forward" or "backward" as far as the laws of nature are concerned and consistent pictures of subatomic events can be drawn up in which particles move forward in time and antiparticles move backward.

Could it be, then, that the photonium cosmic egg, with a baryon number of zero, breaks up into two smaller eggs, one of neutronium and one of antineutronium, and that the former moves forward in time and the latter backward, so that the two are out of reach of each other before they can interact? The neutronium egg with a positive baryon number can be called a "cosmon," while the antineutronium egg with a negative baryon number can be called an "anticosmon."

We can picture the cosmon and anticosmon as both undergoing expansion and as continuing to separate along the time axis. We begin with a tiny cosmon and anticosmon, both close to the zero point on the time axis. As they move apart, they grow larger and larger and more and more separated.*

* Since this chapter first appeared in print, I have discovered that F. R. Stannard of University College, London, is speculating on the existence of such a "negative-time" universe on a more rigorous basis than any I can handle.

For the moment let's concentrate on the cosmon (our Universe). As it expands, the various forms of energy are spread out within it more and more evenly. We express this fact by saying that entropy increases and, indeed, entropy has sometimes been called "time's arrow." If entropy increases, you know time is moving forward.

But when the cosmon begins to contract, all the atomic and subatomic processes that took place during expansion begin to reverse. Entropy then begins to decrease and time begins to run backward.

In other words the cosmon moves forward in time when it is expanding, and backward when it is contracting. The anticosmon (behaving symmetrically) moves backward in time when it is expanding, and forward in time when it is contracting. Each does this over and over again.

Instead of an oscillating Universe, we have an oscillating double-Universe, the two oscillations being exactly in phase, and both Universes coming together to form a combined cosmic egg of photonium.

But if this picture takes care of baryon number, it does not take care of energy. The law of conservation of energy is the most fundamental generalization we know and no matter how I have sliced things so far, the Universe, cosmon and anticosmon combined, is made up of energy.

If the cosmon consists of 1.6×10^{79} neutrons and their descendant particles, and the anticosmon consists of 1.6×10^{79} antineutrons and their descendant particles, then the total energy content of the photonium cosmic egg formed by the coming together of the cosmon and anticosmon must be something like 4.8×10^{76} ergs, and that must always exist, at all stages of the cosmon-anticosmon separation, expansion, contraction, and coalescence.

That is the final hurdle for Asimov's Cosmogonic Principle, for in the photonium cosmic egg all conserved quantities, *except* energy, can be set equal to zero.

How, then, can one set the energy equal to zero as well? To do so, one must postulate something we might call negative-energy.

There is no such thing *as far as we know*. It has never been observed. Nevertheless, the Principle makes its existence necessary.

In a Universe consisting only of negative-energy, all the manifestations would be broadly identical with those in our own Universe consisting of ordinary energy. However, if a sample of ordinary energy and of negative-energy were brought together they would cancel each other and produce Nothing.

There are familiar cases of partial cancellation of physical properties. Two billiard balls moving in opposite directions at equal speeds, and coated with glue to make them stick on collision, will, if they collide head-on, come to a dead halt. Momentum will have been canceled out (but the energy of motion of the billiard balls will be converted to heat). Two sound beams, or light beams, exactly out of phase, will combine to form silence, or darkness (but the energy content of the wave forms will be converted into heat).

In all these partial cancellations, the energy—most fundamental of all—always remains. Well, in the case of the combination of energy and negative-energy, cancellation will be complete. There will be left *Nothing!*

Negative-energy is made up of negative-photons, which can break down to form negative-neutrons and negative-antineutrons. The negative-neutrons can break down to form negative-matter which can be built up to negative-stars and negative-galaxies, forming a negative-cosmon. Negative-antineutrons can break down to form negative-antimatter which will build up to a negative-anticosmon.

Suppose a cosmon and anticosmon contract and combine to form a photonium cosmic egg. A negative-cosmon and a negative-anticosmon can contract to form an antiphotonium cosmic egg. The two cosmic eggs, photonium and antiphotonium can then combine to form Nothing!

We are then left with no cosmic egg at all! We are left with Nothing!

In the beginning was Nothing and this Nothing formed a photonium cosmic egg and an antiphotonium cosmic egg. The photonium cosmic egg behaved as already described, forming a cosmon moving forward in time and an anticosmon moving backward in time. The antiphotonium cosmic egg must behave analogously, forming a negative-cosmon moving forward in time and a negative-anticosmon moving backward in time.

But if the cosmon and negative-cosmon are both moving forward in time why don't they combine and cancel out to Nothing? It seems to me they must remain separate and this separation may come about through gravitational repulsion. So far, we know of gravitational attraction only, and there is no such thing (as far as we know) as gravitational repulsion. If, however, there is negative-energy, and if negative-matter is formed from it, perhaps a gravitational repulsion can also exist and be expressed between matter and negative-matter.

As the cosmon and negative-cosmon expand, gravitational repulsion drives them steadily apart, perhaps, along the space axis (see Figure 1), while both move together up the time axis. Similarly, the anticosmon and negative-anticosmon drive steadily apart along the space axis as they move downward along the time axis.

As Figure 1 shows, the result is rather like a four-leaf clover (which is the significance of the title of this chapter, in case you've been wondering all along).

Once the various Universes pass their expansion peak and begin to contract again, it is possible that not only time is reversed, but the gravitational effect as well. There are theories advanced by important physicists to the effect that gravitational force may be weakening with time and could it be, therefore, that it reaches zero at expansion peak and that during contraction matter repels matter and negative-matter repels negative-matter, while matter attracts negative-matter?

You might object at once by asking how the cosmon, for

instance, will contract, if all its parts experience a mutual repulsion. To which I reply, why not? Right now the cosmon is expanding even though all its parts experience a mutual attraction. Perhaps the cosmon and its sister Universes are so arranged that the grand expansion or contraction is always in opposition to the force of gravity. The force of gravity is incredibly weak and it may be its fate always to be overborne by other forces and effects.

However, in the process of contraction, the overall gravitational attraction between cosmon and negative-cosmon on the one hand, and between anticosmon and negative-anticosmon on the other, may bring them together along the space axis just as time reversal brings them together along the time axis.

When cosmon, anticosmon, negative-cosmon, and negative-anticosmon all come together, they produce—Nothing.

In the Beginning, there is Nothing.

In the End, there is Nothing.

But if we begin with Nothing, why doesn't it stay Nothing?

Why should it? We can say that $0+0=0$, and that $+1+(-1)=0$. Both $0+0$ and $+1+(-1)$ are equivalent ways of saying "zero" and why should one be any more "real" or "natural" than the other? The situation can slide from Nothing to Four-Leaf Clover without difficulty, for no essential has been changed by that transition.

But why should the shift come at one time rather than another? The mere fact that it comes at a particular time means that something has made it shift.

Indeed? What do you mean by time? Time and space only exist in connection with the expansion and contraction of the leaves of the Four-Leaf Clover. When the leaves don't exist, neither does time nor space.

In the Beginning, there is Nothing—not even time or space.

The Four-Leaf Clover comes into existence at no particular time and in no particular place. When it is in existence, time and space exist in a cycle of expansion and contraction that

FIGURE 1—THE FOUR-LEAF CLOVER

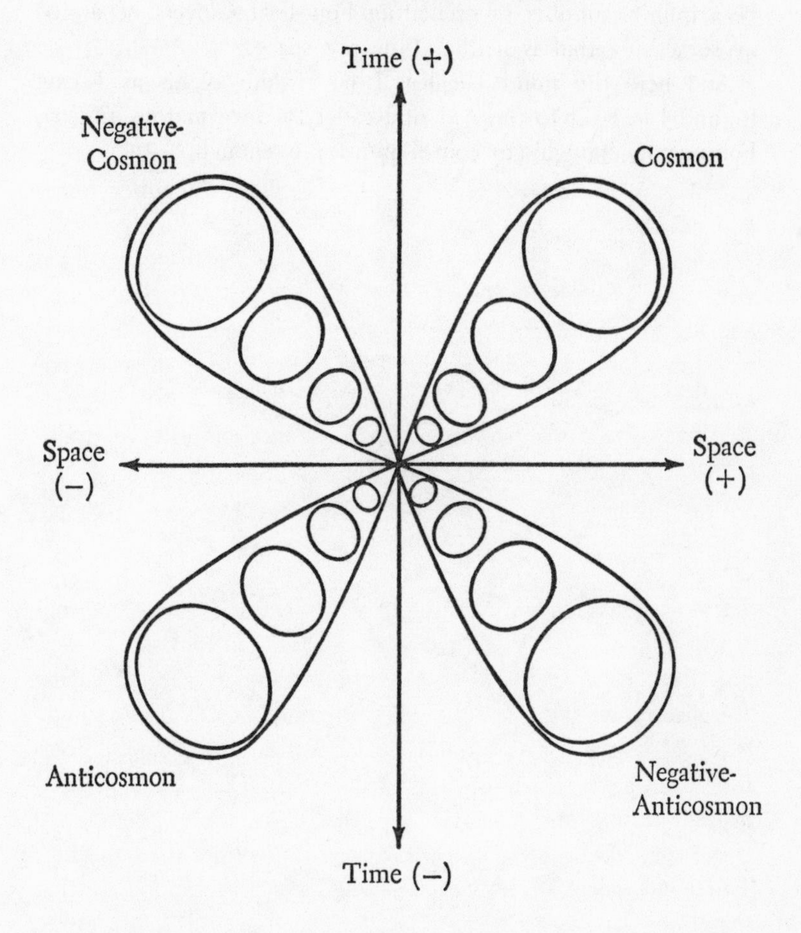

takes eighty billion years. There is then a timeless, spaceless interval and again an expansion and contraction. Since there is nothing we can do with a timeless, spaceless interval, we can eliminate it and consider the cycles of expansion and contraction to be following immediately upon one another. We then have an oscillating quadruple-Universe, an oscillating Four-Leaf Clover.

And who says only one need exist? There are no limits, no

bounds, no ends, no edges to Nothingness. There may therefore be a infinite number of oscillating Four-Leaf Clovers, separated by something that is neither time nor space.

And here the mind boggles. I have gone as far as I care to, and I leave it to the Ardent Reader to carry matters further. For myself, enough (to coin a phrase) is enough.

4. IMPOSSIBLE, THAT'S ALL!

As everyone knows, I am, as yet, still in my late youth, and nothing suits me less than to play the role of conventional graybeard—the fuddy-duddy scientist with the closed mind.

And yet circumstances occasionally force me into what seems to be such a role. For instance, I was watching the first episode of *It's About Time* once. This is a TV farce, which had its season in 1966, and which dealt with a couple of bumbling astronauts who find themselves in a mythical Stone Age in which cavemen talk English and consort with dinosaurs.

This was explained by saying that the astronauts had inadvertently traveled faster than light. As one of them said to the other, "Einstein's theory states that if you go faster than light, time turns backward."

There was no canned laughter at that line but, naturally, I laughed anyway, and my young daughter, who was also watching, wanted to know why I laughed.

I said offhandedly, "You can't go faster than light."

She said, "Why not?"

"Because you just can't," I explained.

"With scientists making new inventions all the time, why can't you someday?"

I came out with the clinching ace, "Because it's impossible, that's all."

Which she promptly trumped with a lofty "*Nothing* is impossible!"

I've heard that argument before, too. I've lost track of the number of letters that have reached me demanding, "*Why* can't you go faster than light?" "How do you *know* you can't go faster than light?" "What makes you think that *someday* we won't break the time-barrier?"

I've got to disappoint them all by standing firm on the you-can't-go-faster-than-light thesis. And I know people turn away from me in disappointment wondering if perhaps I'm just a member of the Scientific Establishment—a fuddy-duddy scientist with a closed mind.

So let's talk about the impossible.

For instance, we can start with 2+2. That equals 4, right? Add another 2 and you have 6, and then 8, and then 10, and so on ad infinitum. If we start with 0 and add 2's one at a time, we build up the set of "even numbers" which is, by this definition, 2, 4, 6, 8, 10, 12, 14, 16 . . .

You can see, intuitively (that is, just by looking at them), that all even numbers are divisible by 2. Or, since you define an even number as being of the form 2+2+2+2 . . . then you see you can convert that to 2(1+1+1+1 . . .) for as many or as few 2's in the sum as you wish. Consequently, all even numbers are divisible by 2.*

Now suppose you want to add any two even numbers: 2+4, or 72+106; or 8,640,772+54; or any two at all. What can you say about the answer? Well, any even number can be written as the sum of a series of 2's so that you are adding 2+2+2+2 . . . and 2+2+2+2 . . . with the result that the sum must be both sets of 2's added together: 2+2+2+2 . . . +2+2+2 +2 . . .

Therefore, since the sum of the even numbers is also built

* I have a feeling that this reasoning would not be sufficiently rigorous to satisfy a real mathematician, but I'm coming out with the right answer, so never mind.

up out of 2's, it, too, is even. In other words: *The sum of two even numbers is even.* In fact, it is easy to reason out the generalization that the number obtained by adding or subtracting any number of even numbers must be even—provided we are willing to call 0 an even number as well as such negative numbers as -2, -4, -6, and so on.

What is an odd number? That can be defined as any number that is 1 greater than an even number and that therefore cannot be built up out of 2's alone. The odd numbers are $2+1$, $2+2+1$; $2+2+2+1$; and so on or 3, 5, 7, 9, 11 . . . If we call 0 an even number, then 1 is an odd number since $1=0+1$. And if negative numbers such as -2, -4, -6 . . . are even, then negative numbers such as -1, -3, -5 . . . are odd.

Obviously, if you add or subtract any number of even numbers you cannot get an odd number, because in dealing with numbers built up of 2's only, where is that 1 (which is an integral portion of the definition of odd numbers) to come from?

So we conclude: it is *impossible* to obtain an odd number by adding or subtracting any number of even numbers.

It is no use at all in saying to me: "How do you know? Have you tried every possible combination of even numbers? Maybe there is some queer combination of unusual even numbers which you've never investigated and which give an odd number when added together."

The answer is, "I don't have to investigate every possible combination of even numbers. The definition of even and odd numbers is expressed in such a way as to make it impossible to obtain odd numbers by adding and subtracting even numbers."

And if they then say, "But I have here a very complicated addition of twenty different even numbers and the sum is odd," I must then answer, "You've made an arithmetical error."

They may then say plaintively, "But how can you tell? Won't you add it up and see for yourself?"

I suppose I could then add it up just to show them their

arithmetical error and urge them to choke on it, but I would be completely within my rights to refuse and say, "The arithmetical error is there. Find it for yourself. I won't waste my time."

Naturally, the case of evens adding up to evens is so simple and open-and-shut a case, that no one with the slightest arithmetical intuition would argue with me. They would nod their heads and say, "Of course."

But when things grow more complicated, chances of bitterness arise.

Thus, mathematicians have shown that it is impossible to square the circle, duplicate the cube, or trisect an angle by use of a compass and straight-edge alone. This is a much more complicated demonstration than that which suffices to show that even numbers cannot be summed to yield an odd number, but it is of the same general type. The conclusion is just as certain and just as indisputable and no real mathematician argues with it.

Nevertheless, any number of amateurs come up every year with demonstrations that purport to prove that the circle can be squared, or the cube duplicated, or the angle trisected with compass and straight-edge alone. Often they send these demonstrations to mathematicians who may then send them back promptly without bothering to look at them.

The amateur may feel that he is the subject of a conspiracy, the victim of professionals who won't even *look* at the evidence. As it happens, the mathematician doesn't have to. He knows a fallacy is present somewhere, but sometimes it isn't easy to find such a fallacy in a hundred pages of reasoning and diagrams. Why spend hours or days of valuable time in the hunt for something that *must* be there?

Let's look at a second kind of "impossible" now. Since I've mentioned fallacies let's consider one in detail. In other words, let's consider a line of reasoning, each step of which seems perfectly legitimate, but which reaches a final conclusion that is patently ridiculous.

To do this, let's take the simplest algebraic fallacy I know; one that is so simple, even I managed to catch it at once when I was first faced with it.

We start with two quantities, a and b, which we set equal to each other:

$$a=b \qquad \text{(Equation 1)}$$

We can multiply both sides of an equation by the same value, without affecting the equality, so let's multiply both sides by a:

$$a^2=ab \qquad \text{(Equation 2)}$$

We can subtract the same value from both sides of an equation without affecting the equality, so let's subtract b^2 from both sides:

$$a^2-b^2=ab-b^2 \qquad \text{(Equation 3)}$$

It so happens that the expression a^2-b^2 can be obtained by multiplying $a+b$ and $a-b$, so that a^2-b^2 can be written $(a+b)(a-b)$. And $ab-b^2$ is the product of b and $a-b$. Now we have:

$$(a+b)(a-b)=b(a-b) \qquad \text{(Equation 4)}$$

We can divide both sides of an equation by the same value without affecting the equality so let's divide by $a-b$. This means that the $a-b$ factor on both sides of the equation drop out and we are left with:

$$a+b=b \qquad \text{(Equation 5)}$$

Since $a=b$ (Equation 1), we can say that $a+b$ is the same as $b+b$. Therefore Equation 5 becomes

$$b+b=b \qquad \text{(Equation 6)}$$
$$2b=b \qquad \text{(Equation 7)}$$

Now, if we divide both sides of Equation 7 by *b*, we are left with our grand and ridiculous conclusion that:

$$2=1 \qquad \text{(Equation 8)}$$

What's wrong? Look back a bit and see where I said, "We can divide both sides of an equation by the same value without affecting the equality so let's divide by $a-b$."

But earlier I had said that $a=b$, so that $a-b$ is equal to $b-b$, which is 0. Therefore, when I say, "Let's divide by $a-b$," I am saying, "Let's divide by 0," and that is not allowed in mathematics.

You might object at once and say, "*Why* isn't it allowed?"

The answer is a simple one. If division by 0 were to be allowed then it becomes possible to prove that 2=1, as I have just shown you. Indeed, it becomes possible to prove that any number at all, positive, negative, fractional, irrational, imaginary, or transcendental is equal to any other number at all. Such a mathematical system in which all numbers are equal has no use and mathematicians don't want it.

In working up the rules that govern the various mathematical operations then, mathematicians find that the easiest way to avoid such an unwanted occurrence is simply to forbid division by zero.

So we have a different sense of the word "impossible." Division by zero isn't impossible in the sense that it can't be done in the manipulation of symbols. I did it just above when I divided both sides of an equation by $a-b$. It's impossible in the sense that it breaks the rules of the game. As soon as it is done, the name of the game is no longer mathematics. One can't divide by zero *and* engage in mathematics at the same time.

Now let's pass on to physics. In mathematics, one creates an ideal world which may have its analogies to reality, but need not necessarily. In physics, however, one must be guided by one's best estimate of what reality is and then describe it as best one can.

As a result of *experience* (not deduction from basic premises, or definition for the sake of convenience) certain generalizations can be made about the physical universe. These are usually called "laws of nature," which is a pretentious term dating from the overconfidence of the so-called Age of Reason. Actually, they are just generalizations.

The most powerful generalization we know of can be stated thusly: *The total energy present in a closed system is constant* (where a closed system, in this case, is one into which energy cannot enter and from which energy cannot depart, so that the only truly closed system is the Universe as a whole).

This is the famous "law of conservation of energy" and it introduces an "impossibility." We can say: "It is impossible to create or destroy energy."

This statement, however, while casually made I don't know how many times by I don't know how many people, is not absolutely true. The creation of destruction of energy is not an impossibility in the sense that it would represent a contradiction in terms (as in the case of the mathematical odd and even) or defy a convention (as in the case of division by zero). What is really meant is that the experience of mankind has failed to show a single instance in which the creation or destruction of energy has indisputably been brought about. But the experience of mankind is not infinite and there may be unlooked-for conditions under which that experience could be shown to be insufficient. What then?

On two different occasions, since the law of conservation of energy was announced, it seemed that it might have to be abandoned as not, after all, an absolutely valid generalization. First, scientists discovered, at the end of the nineteenth century, that the energy given off by radioactive materials seemed to come from nowhere. Was energy being created? Einstein demonstrated this was not so in 1905 when he suggested that mass was a type of energy, and that the energy given off in radioactivity (or other nuclear reactions) was balanced by an equivalent loss of mass. This was eventually shown to be correct.

Then, in the 1920s, scientists discovered that beta particles were being fired out of atoms with less energy than they ought to have. Was energy being destroyed? Pauli suggested in 1931 that this was not so, explaining the energy loss by postulating the existence of a new particle, the neutrino, which was actually detected a quarter century later.

Yet what if the law of conservation of energy had been disproved and cast aside on either of these occasions? What would that mean?

It is important to remember that science consists of observations *and* theories, and that the destruction of a theory does *not* mean the destruction of the observations. Many non-scientists are confused in this respect. Since conservation of energy requires us to eat food and breathe oxygen if we are to live, there is the vague thought that if one could only find the law to be false, one would suddenly no longer need to eat food or breathe oxygen.

Yet the necessity of eating and breathing is an observed fact that is independent of theory. If any generalization accounting for the necessity is proven false, then we will simply need another generalization accounting for that same necessity.

For instance, throughout the nineteenth century, chemists worked on the basis that the law of conservation of mass was fundamental. This held that the total mass of any closed system was constant. All their experience and observation seemed to prove to nineteenth-century chemists that this generalization was valid.

Then came Einstein in 1905 and showed that mass could be converted into energy so that mass, in itself, was not conserved.

Did that show the experience of the nineteenth-century chemists to have been ludicrously wrong? Not at all. You can walk into a laboratory today—right now—and work with those chemical phenomena known in the nineteenth century and make use of techniques available in the nineteenth century, and you will be unable to demonstrate the flaw in the law of conservation of mass, even though you know what you are looking for. That flaw appeared only with the discovery of nuclear reactions, which involve much greater mass-energy interconversions than do chemical reactions, and nineteenth-century chemists did not know of nuclear reactions.

In fact, it is safe to say that whenever a useful generalization is upset, one which has withstood the probings of scientists for a good, long time, it is upset in regions of investigation that have been freshly opened up and which the older scientists were unaware of. What's more the older generalization would remain just as useful as ever in those areas in which it had been established.

Thus, in ordinary chemical reactions, chemists still work on the assumption that mass is conserved, even though they know that it isn't *really*. The degree to which it is not conserved in ordinary reactions is so tiny that it can safely be ignored. Similarly if the law of conservation of energy had stumbled and fallen over the matter of the neutrino, it would nevertheless have remained useful, and would have continued to be used, in the ordinary world of macroscopic physics.

A few years back, on the other hand, something called the "Dean drive" was highly touted in science fiction circles. It purported to be a device which converted rotational motion into one-way linear motion, thus breaking the law of conservation of angular momentum and the law of conservation of linear momentum. Both laws have held up under the intense scrutiny of any number of physicists for three centuries and the chance that they could be broken on a large scale in just those areas where they have been under scrutiny longest and most intensely is virtually nil. Consequently I remained stubbornly uninterested in the Dean drive and willingly left its investigation to others who might, just possibly, also be interested in finding some way to square the circle with compass and straight-edge.

Next consider the three laws of motion advanced by Isaac Newton in the 1680s. For over two centuries the keenest efforts of the keenest minds found no exceptions to Newton's laws of motion. Indeed, every relevant experiment supported them and the complex structure of mechanics was based upon them. By 1900 it seemed extremely unlikely that any significant flaw could have been found in the laws of motion *in the areas in which they had been studied.*

We all know, though, that in 1905, Einstein revised Newton's laws of motion by introducing his own relativistic view of the Universe. This revision, however, was only significant in new areas beyond the ken of eighteenth- and nineteenth-century physics. It was only significant, for instance, at great velocities which could not adequately be investigated by Newton and his followers with the techniques at their disposal. At all ordinary velocities (say less than a thousand miles a second) Einstein's version of laws of motion does not differ significantly from Newton's.

According to Newton's laws of motion, for instance, different velocities could be added together according to the rules of simple arithmetic. Suppose a train is passing you at twenty miles an hour and a boy on the train throws a ball at twenty miles an hour in the direction of the train's motion. To the body, moving with the train, the ball is moving twenty miles an hour. To you, however, watching from side of the tracks, the velocity of the train and the ball add together, and the ball is moving at the rate of forty miles an hour. In other words, you can say that the velocity of a ball varies from observer to observer according to the velocity of the source of the thrown ball relative to the observer.

What spoiled the Newtonian view was the fact that what works for thrown balls does not seem to work for light. As Michelson and Morley showed in 1886 the velocity of light was always measured at the same value by any observer regardless of the motion of the light-source relative to that observer.

Thus, to put it simply, a moving flashlight will throw out a beam of light that will travel at the same velocity as the beam of light emerging from a stationary flashlight. What's more, a moving flashlight will send out a beam of light at the same velocity in the direction of its motion as against the direction of its motion.

To be sure, Newton knew about light, but he could not use it to check his laws of motion. The comparative velocity of light beams moving in different directions could not be measured with sufficient accuracy to test those laws until Michelson invented his interferometer.

All attempts to explain this behavior of light by means of Newton's laws failed, and Einstein decided to work backward. He said, in effect, "Let us begin by accepting the behavior of light as a fact. Let's suppose that its measured velocity in a vacuum is independent of the motion of its source. How, now, can we arrange the laws of motion to allow for that, while still allowing for all the facts concerning thrown balls that have been observed over the last three centuries?"

He thereupon worked up a view of the Universe in which objects grew shorter in the direction of their motion as their velocity relative to an observer increase. They would also grow more massive, and would experience a slower passage of time.

This seems to be against "common sense" but what we call "common sense" is merely the experience we have gained concerning objects moving at low velocities.* The changes in length, mass, and time-rate are so small at ordinary velocities that they cannot be detected. Working at ordinary velocities, one can assume, without significant error, that the Newtonian laws of motion hold.

But the Einsteinian view depends on the validity of his basic assumption. What if the velocity of light in a vacuum is *not* independent of the motion of its source?

Well, for one thing no one has yet observed any difference in light's velocity in a vacuum with motion of the source—and believe me, people have looked, if only because the discovery of

* This is like the "common sense" that tells us the Earth is flat because we commonly deal with portions so small that their gentle curvature goes unnoticed.

such a difference would mean an automatic Nobel Prize. Every time new techniques of greater delicacy are discovered, one of the first things done is to check the velocity of light from a moving source. So far Einstein's assumption has always held up.

Then, too, you can judge the value of an assumption by the accuracy of the conclusions one can deduce from it. The Einsteinian view makes certain predictions concerning the behavior of particles at great velocities. Such velocities were never observed by eighteenth- and nineteenth-century physicists, which is why the Newtonian view survived. With the discovery of radioactivity, however, scientists found at their disposal crowds of subatomic particles moving at velocities of many thousands of miles per second.

Such particles, moving at such velocities, would have one set of properties according to the Newtonian view, and quite another set according to the Einsteinian view. Careful measurement showed the Einsteinian view to be correct every time—and to a high degree of accuracy.

Even Einstein's suggestion that mass and energy are interconvertible is based on his assumption about the speed of light, and that too has held up exactly all the way from delicate measurements on individual subatomic particles to the explosion of a hundred-megaton hydrogen bomb.

Einstein's special theory of relativity is thus established beyond a reasonable doubt.

Can it be, though, that in the future, Einstein's view will be found to be a mere approximation as Newton's view was—although Einstein's would be, of course, a closer approximation?

Yes, of course that is possible. But the failure of the Einsteinian approximation would become evident only in areas of investigation beyond those in which it has stood up over and over, and would probably require techniques of measurement outside our present knowledge. What's more, any new and more accurate view of the Universe, would leave the Einsteinian view close enough in all the areas in which it seems close enough now.

Now to get to the nub of the article.

One of the consequences of the Einsteinian view is that nothing material can be measured as going faster than the speed of light in a vacuum, nor can information in any form be sent from point A to point B in less time than light (in a vacuum) could travel from point A to point B.

It is this which is usually translated into the briefer and more arrogant phrase: "You can't go faster than the speed of light."

This view is backed in two ways.

First, nothing material has ever been measured as moving faster than the speed of light in a vacuum. Speeding subatomic particles approach the speed of light quite closely under some conditions, and velocities equal to 99.99+ percent that of light in a vacuum have been measured—but never any velocity quite reaching that of light, let alone surpassing it. If it were possible to go faster than light, it would be extremely puzzling to fail to find an occasional particle which just manages to go an extra few miles a second in order to surpass light's velocity. If, however, the velocity of light is an absolute speed-limit, the failure of any particle to exceed it, no matter how close it gets, becomes understandable.

Second, if anything went faster than light, the entire structure of the Einsteinian view would be shattered, but it would not alter all the observations that have been made in the last sixty years that are in perfect accord with the theory.

We would then be faced with the problem of working out another theory which would explain all the observed facts that Einstein's theory explains so neatly, and yet one which also allowed motion faster than light.

That would be so difficult a task that I don't think there is a physicist alive today who would be willing to try his hand at it —or who would succeed if he did.

Therefore, one can conclude that the chances of anything being able to move faster than the speed of light, while not impossible in the mathematical sense, are so vanishingly small, that when I am belligerently asked *why* nothing can go faster than the speed of light, I find that the best possible short explanation is:

"Because it's impossible, that's all!"

Note: Since this chapter first appeared in print, G. Feinberg of Columbia University sent me a paper in which he worked out the theoretical nature of a Universe in which nothing can go *slower* than light. Such a "fast-Universe" could be made to fit Einstein's theory. Feinberg cannot suggest, as yet, any easy way of detecting the fast-Universe from our own slow-Universe, or vice versa. Here we have another case of multiple Universes out of touch, as in the case of the anticosmons and negative-cosmons of the previous chapter.

5. A MATTER OF SCALE

Every time I attend a large science fiction convention, I spend at least a couple of hours wandering through the exhibitions of old science fiction magazines and books. I rarely buy anything—alas, my library is not geared to this particular luxury—but I harvest a rich crop of nostalgia.

Old magazine issues rise before by eyes in the flesh. The names of old revered authors return. Old stories, old plots, old styles bring back a whiff of youthful star-shine and soft retrospective sighs.

At the 1966 Cleveland convention, for instance, I came across one of the "Posi and Nega" stories by Joseph W. Skidmore. For those too young to know, they were tales of the adventures and misadventures of two subatomic particles. Posi was the positively charged proton and Nega the negatively charged electron (get it?). To complicate matters, Posi was a male and Nega a female, and Skidmore combined romance and melodrama with points of elementary chemistry.

Believe me when I tell you that when I started studying chemistry in earnest, it was hard for me to think of subatomic particles impersonally, thanks to these stories. It was even harder for me to abandon another science fictional treatment of the atom—a chestnut of the 1920s and 1930s in which the atom was viewed as a tiny Solar system.

In these stories, our hero reduced himself in size, went visiting on an electronic planet circling a protonic Sun, found a Zenda-like world of romance, and a beautiful girl in flowing, diaphanous draperies. Eventually he had to return to our own world and the girl was lost, but the attempt to find her again was always good for a sequel.

(I took this quite seriously for a few years and was convinced the Solar system was a fluorine super-atom because it contained nine planets. I ignored the asteroids.)

Actually, this atomic Solar system was not a science fictional invention at all. In 1904, when scientists were trying to fit the newly discovered subatomic particles into the atom, a Japanese physicist, H. Nagaoka, suggested a structure that was something like the Solar system. This caught the fancy of those sections of the lay public that were interested in such matters. It went out the window once Niels Bohr worked out the first quantum-view of the atom in 1913, but the outmoded Nagaoka version persisted for at least a quarter century more in the minds of s.f. writers—a neat (if specialized) example of cultural lag.

But science itself has chestnuts and cultural lags too. For instance, I suppose that one could easily work one's way through elementary astronomy books for the layman and find a dozen in the first dozen minutes which contain a passage that begins: "Imagine the Sun to be the size of a basketball—"

There is very often an attempt to give a notion of the scale of the Solar system in understandable terms, you see, and invariably we have the Sun as a basketball, Jupiter and Saturn as oranges, Uranus and Neptune as plums, Earth, and Venus as grapes—all scattered over a level field.

This is bad on two counts. First, it isn't quantitative and fixes the thought that planets are pieces of fruit, which is even worse than presenting them as electrons. Secondly, it is useful only for giving a notion of the scale of the Solar system.

This sort of Solar-system-centered scale dates back to the eighteenth-century attitude that only the Solar system counted and that the stars could be dismissed in a final chapter with some constellation pictures.

By the first half of this century, Solar system studies almost vanished into oblivion,* while the stars and galaxies took the center of the stage. But did the basketball with its circling fruit change? You can bet your parallax it didn't. Writers kept right on using it with blind automatism. That's cultural lag too.

But now I have finally come across an interesting scale model of another sort, altogether, one that takes into account the Universe rather than the Solar system. You'll find it on page 34 of a brand-new book entitled *Intelligent Life in the Universe* by I. S. Shklovskii and Carl Sagan; the product of a most unusual (perhaps even unique) collaboration by mail between two first-class astronomers, one Soviet and one American. I recommend it with all my might to everyone within sight of these words. I've read it through twice with the greatest of pleasure, though ordinarily it is hard for me to find time to read even the most necessary books once.

The passage on the scale set my mind to jumping restlessly, so now I would like to toy with the notion of scale models of astronomical objects in this article.

We can begin in the usual fashion, except that I scorn basketballs. Instead, let's make the Sun 1 foot in diameter rather than the 4½ billion feet it actually is; a scale reduction of 4,500,000,000:1 which we can call the "foot-scale." On the basis of this foot-scale, we can present in Table 4 the diameters of the various planets and the distance of each from the Sun:

* At midcentury, Solar system studies staged a remarkable comeback, thanks chiefly to the use of rockets and satellites and is now flourishing with almost unbelievable vigor.

TABLE 4: THE FOOT-SCALE

Planet	*Diameter (inches)*	*Mean Distance from Sun (feet)*
Mercury	0.043	41
Venus	0.105	78
Earth	0.110	107
Mars	0.058	163
Ceres	0.0062	300
Jupiter	1.2	560
Saturn	1.0	1000
Uranus	0.42	2050
Neptune	0.41	3200
Pluto	0.06(?)	4250

We have a rather dramatic picture of the Solar system, out of which we can pick a few salient points. Saturn, for instance, comes out oddly even. If the Sun is pictured as a globe a foot across, Saturn is a globe an inch across and a thousand feet away.

Earth is only 1/9 of an inch across and about 100 feet away. What's more, on this scale, our Moon is about 1/30 of an inch across and is about 6½ inches from the Earth.

But Jupiter is not only 1.2 inches across but it has a satellite system that stretches outward enormously. On the foot-scale the farthest known satellite from Jupiter is 17 feet away. The Jovian system of satellites requires a total space of 34 feet to move around in.

Pluto is nearly a mile from the Sun on the foot-scale and the Solar system (counting out only to Pluto's orbit and ignoring comets and undiscovered planets) is 1.6 miles across, from side to side of the farthest orbit.

To put it another way, the area swept out by all the planets as they circle the Sun would, on this foot-scale, be just 2 square miles or about one-tenth the area of the island of Manhattan.

Suppose, for instance, we picture our foot-wide globe in the center of Manhattan's Central Park (and I hope that my readers from other sections of the country forgive my provincialism). All the planets out to Saturn would have their orbits entirely within the park. The three outermost would venture outside the eastern and western boundaries of the park, but even Pluto would remain within Manhattan and not reach either the East River or the Hudson River.

This is indeed a convenient way of picturing the Solar system, but it breaks down completely if we try to move on to the stars.

If the Sun is a foot across, an astronomical unit (the mean distance of the Earth from the Sun) is just over a hundred feet, but a light-year is 1300 *miles,* a parsec is 4200 *miles,* and the nearest star is 5500 *miles* away.

In other words, if we place our foot-scale Solar system in Central Park, the nearest star (the Alpha Centauri system) is in Jerusalem.

Maybe this gives you some idea of the distance of the stars, but it is an inadequate one for at best it can deal with only the very nearest ones. For anything beyond, we run out of Earth's surface, and must venture into space.

Thus, instead of imagining Alpha Centauri at a distance that can be reached by trudging along Earth's surface, we can imagine it out in the direction of the Moon. On the foot-scale, Alpha Centauri would be about 1/40 of the way to the Moon. There would be only about 8000 stars between the Central Park Solar system and the Moon's orbit and this doesn't even begin to take care of the billions of stars in our Galaxy.

In other words, the foot-scale leaves us in astronomic distances outside the Solar system itself and we will have to do better.

Let's reduce our scale by a factor of 100,000 or so and make the total diameter of Pluto's orbit just 1 inch. The Sun on this scale would be less than 1/8000 of an inch across. It would, in fact, be roughly the size of one of the larger bacteria. On this "bacterial-scale," stars would be microscopic in size for the most part and only the larger red giants would remain visible to the naked eye. (The giant star, Antares, would be about 1/16 inch in diameter.)

On the bacterial-scale, a light-year would be equal to just about 800 inches. Here, in Table 5, is a list of the distances of some familiar bright stars on this scale:

TABLE 5: THE BACTERIAL-SCALE

Star	*Distance (miles)*
Alpha Centauri	0.055
Sirius	0.11
Procyon	0.14
Altair	0.20
Vega	0.34
Pollux	0.42
Arcturus	0.51
Capella	0.54
Canopus	1.25
Betelgeuse	3.5
Rigel	6.9

In visualizing these distances, keep firmly fixed in mind that you are dealing with separations between bacteria-sized objects. If the Sun were only as large as a bacterium, Arcturus (also as large as a bacterium) would be half a mile away. (Actually, the stars listed in the table are the particularly large bright ones so they would be somewhat larger than bacteria, but this is quite exceptional. The large majority of stars would be bacterial in size on this scale.)

Or let's put it another way. There are 39 star systems, counting the Sun itself, known to exist within seventeen light-years of ourselves. (Eight of these systems are double stars and two are triple stars so that there are 51 stars altogether.)

If we consider these stars as strewn within a sphere which is 17 light-years in radius and has the Sun at the center, we have a sphere with a volume of just about 20,000 cubic light-years.

The amount of space per star system is 500 cubic light-years and the average distance between star systems in the neighborhood of the Sun is therefore the cube root of 500 or roughly 8 light-years.

If we transfer everything to the bacterial-scale, we see that the stars about us can be pictured as bacteria-sized objects (often in isolation, sometimes in clusters of two or three) separated by an average distance of 530 feet.

If you imagined Central Park covered by a roof one-third of a mile high at all points, the volume of space included under that dome would equal, on the bacterial-scale, the 17-light-year-radius sphere I have just mentioned. In this stretch of space overlying Central Park, imagine 51 bacteria floating (a few in groups of two or three) and *nothing else*. There is your picture of starry space.

In the real Universe, the Sun is moving through space at the velocity of about 12 miles per second relative to the other stars of the neighborhood. On the bacterial-scale, this would represent a motion of $\frac{1}{20}$ of an inch a year.

Very well, then; imagine these bacteria, separated by an average distance of 530 feet, moving in random directions at a velocity of $\frac{1}{20}$ of an inch a year (relative to the center of mass of the group) and try to estimate the chances of one of these bacteria just happening to collide with another. How long would it take for such a collision to happen? Eons of time, obviously.

It was this sort of argument that gave the old theory of the origin of the Solar system through the collision, or near collision, of two stars a special significance. The likelihood of such an event was so small that in all our Galaxy in all its existence, only perhaps ten stellar systems might have formed in this manner. It was easy to believe that in only ten stellar systems, the planet Earth might be the only one comfortably suited for life, and Earth might therefore be the only life-bearing world in all the Galaxy. It would just about certainly be the only intelligence-bearing one.

I'm glad the collision theory broke down. The thought of all those hundred billion stars of the Galaxy shining upon empty lifeless space was too wasteful a picture to be endured.

Although the bacterial-scale is fine for giving us a picture of our stellar neighborhood, it isn't really useful if we want to consider the galaxies.

Our own Milky Way Galaxy is a lens-shaped object, about 100,000 light-years across. Our Solar system is some 30,000 light-years from its center, and therefore about 20,000 light-years from one side of the lens. The Galaxy has, at its center, a nucleus containing some nine-tenths of all its stars; a nucleus that is roughly a sphere some 16,000 light-years in diameter.

Outside that nucleus are the flat spiral-arms in which stars are more sparsely strewn than in the nucleus. In the neighborhood of our Sun, these arms are some 3000 light-years thick. The Galactic plane is an imaginary plane slicing the Galaxy in half flat-wise, and our Sun is only about 45 light-years from this plane. (See Figure 2.)

FIGURE 2—THE GALAXY

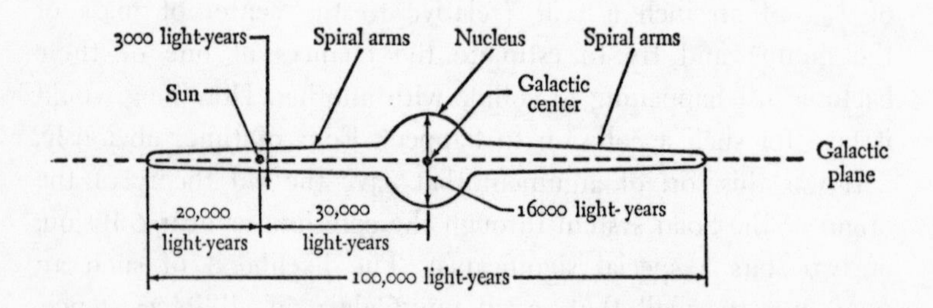

If we want to picture the Galaxy on the bacterial-scale, we find that its full diameter is 1250 miles across and the nucleus is 200 miles thick. We ourselves would be 375 miles from the center, and the thickness of the spiral arms at our position would be about 37 miles.

The cross-sectional area covered by the Galaxy on the bacterial-scale (if we imagine it laid down flat on the Earth's surface—and ignore the curvature of that surface) is some 1,400,000 square miles or just about half the area of the 48 contiguous states. All that area you can imagine as crawling with bacteria, over a hundred billion of them, extending dozens of miles up into the air and dozens of miles down into the ground.

Yet this is too large an object, perhaps, to picture conveniently. It gets worse if you try to visualize the neighboring galaxies on the bacterial-scale. The nearest large one (the Andromeda galaxy) would be no less than 25,000 miles away.

Let us therefore contract the scale still further, and imagine the Sun merely the size of a hydrogen atom, say about 1/250,000,000 of an inch across. On this "atomic-scale," a light-year is not more than 0.0274 inches, or just a bit more than 1/40 of an inch long. The nearest star on the atomic-scale would be about an eighth of an inch away.

This atomic-scale pictures the stars as atom-sized objects separated by an average distance of 0.22 inches. If we pretend that each star is a double star (which doesn't introduce any significant astronomical difference) it is very tempting to try to compare the atomic-scale galaxy with a sample of hydrogen gas, which is made up of hydrogen molecules that are in turn pairs of hydrogen atoms.

At ordinary atmospheric pressure, and at a temperature of 0° C., we can calculate the number of molecules of hydrogen in a given quantity of the gas and, from that, calculate the average separation of molecules. Without giving you the pain of the calculation, I can tell you that the average separation is 0.00000013 inches.

In other words, if we shrank our Galaxy to the point where the stars making it up were the size of hydrogen atoms, the separation between them would be more than a million times as great as between the molecules in a sample of ordinary hydrogen gas. The Galaxy, on the atomic-scale, is an example of a very good vacuum.

But that's just our neighborhood and we are in the sparseness of a spiral arm. What about a globular cluster? Such a cluster is a spherical volume, about 200 light-years across, where as many as 100,000 individual stars are concentrated. Seen in photographs, such clusters resemble heaps of talcum powder, with stars so thickly strewn as to melt together into a uniform blaze. One has the picture of stars jostling each other madly.

But do they?

Such a sphere has a volume of 4,200,000 cubic light-years and there is, therefore, an average volume of 42 light-years per star and an average distance of separation of 3.5 light-years.

This is only the average distance of separation. Stars are increasingly crowded as one approaches the center of a globular cluster, so suppose we say that at the center the average distance of separation between stars drops to only 0.5 light-years.

On the atomic-scale such a separation is equal to 0.014 inches and this is still 100,000 times as great as the separation between molecules of hydrogen in ordinary hydrogen gas under Earthly conditions. Even the center of a globular cluster, then, is comparable to an Earthly vacuum, with a density only one-quintillionth that of hydrogen. Consider, too, that the hydrogen molecules are moving at mile-a-minute velocities, whereas on an atomic scale, the stars in a globular cluster are just about motionless relative to each other. You can see, then, that even at the center of a globular cluster there is not much chance of stellar collisions.

Stars are strewn through the Galactic center with about twice the density found in globular clusters and perhaps, at the very core of our Galaxy, average separations of 0.25 light-years are to be found. The vacuum is still a good one and even at the Galactic center collisions will take place only once every million years or so.

(Nevertheless, the force of gravitation of a volume containing several million crowded stars is incredibly higher than it is over a volume containing several million hydrogen molecules—so that large numbers of stars may conceivably collapse or "implode" to liberate fantastic energies, whereas molecules do not and cannot behave like that. One must not carry analogies too far.)

On the atomic-scale, the Galaxy is 225 feet across and the Sun is about 80 feet from the center. The Galactic nucleus is about 43 feet in diameter and the thickness of the spiral arm here where our Sun is, is about 8 feet.

Even on the atomic-scale, the Galaxy is an impressive object, for if laid flat on the ground, it will cover just about an acre.

The Sun moves around the Galactic center in 220 million years. On the atomic-scale it covers an orbital length of about 500 feet in that 220,000,000 years or about five-hundredths of an inch in a seventy-year lifetime of watching. Obviously the Galaxy will seem motionless under these conditions and, indeed, when we observe the nearby galaxies by telescope, at sizes equivalent to less than the atomic-scale, they do indeed seem motionless.

On the atomic-scale, by the way, the nearest large galaxy, the Andromeda, is almost exactly a mile away. The exploding galaxy M82 is 4¼ miles away. A cluster of galaxies in Virgo is 16 miles away and a giant cluster in Coma Berenices is 81 miles away.

The nearest quasar (see Chapter 2) is perhaps 900 miles away. The farthest known quasar is about 3500 miles away and the edge of the Observable Universe is 5300 miles away.

Even on the atomic-scale, then, with the Galaxy itself quite easily visualizable, the entire Universe is still uncomfortably large, making up a sphere over 10,000 miles across.

Let us take on another shrinkage, then, and obtain our fourth scale. Let us pretend that the Sun is not the size of an atom, but the size of a proton at the center of an atom. It is about 1/25,000,000,000,000 of an inch across and this gives us the "protonic-scale."*

* Shklovskii and Sagan, in the book I mentioned near the beginning of the article, make use of a scale in which Earth's orbit is the size of a hydrogen atom. This is smaller than my atomic-scale but not as small as my protonic-scale.

On the protonic-scale, the Milky Way Galaxy—the entire mighty lens of over 100,000,000,000 stars—shrinks to a mere 0.0274 inches in diameter.

How distances shrink now! The nearest quasar lies at a distance of some 40 feet from the tiny lens of the Galaxy, while the farthest known quasar is at a distance of a bit over 180 feet. The edge of the Observable Universe is a little under 300 feet away.

So if we imagine the stars to be the size of protons, the entire Universe becomes a sphere of 600 feet in diameter and its volume is roughly 100,000,000 cubic feet.

How many galaxies does it contain? Nobody knows, but a good, round guess that I have often seen is 100,000,000,000. This would mean 1000 protonic-scaled galaxies per cubic foot and the average distance between galaxies would be about 1.2 inches.

Actually, the Andromeda galaxy is only about 0.6 inches from us on the protonic-scale and there are a number of small galaxies as close or closer, so the separation of galaxies in our own neighborhood seems less than the average distance I calculated.

Perhaps we lie in a volume where galaxies are strewn more thickly than on the average. We may be part of a huge galaxy of galaxies, a "super-galaxy" beyond the edges of which there is a great deal of relatively empty space until we come to another super-galaxy. In that case, the galactic density within the super-galaxy cannot be considered typical of space generally. There are some astronomers who do think just that.

On the other hand, it may also be that the estimate of 100,000,000,000 galaxies in the Observable Universe errs on the side of conservatism. Perhaps there are a hundred trillion rather than a hundred billion. I, for one, would not be surprised.

Let me make one more quick drop to a fifth and last scale. Suppose our entire Galaxy were the size of an atom. In that ultimate-scale the Observable Universe would be 1/700 of an inch across and the average distance between galaxies would become 0.0000002 inches. This would be very close to the separation of the molecules in ordinary hydrogen under standard conditions.

In other words, if we could only get away from the Universe; get away far enough to see it as a little bubble of microscopic matter—so small that its galaxies were no more than atoms—we would find that we had a tiny droplet of "galaxy gas" with a particle density like that of "ordinary gas."

Which brings us full-circle, at last, and safely home.

Or are we safely home? Ought we perhaps to wonder if the generation of science fiction writers who tried to make Solar systems out of atoms were just being too conservative? Now if they had tried to make galaxies out of them, would they—

But no, that way madness lies!

6. KALEIDOSCOPE IN THE SKY

In 1966 I published a book called *The Universe* which garnered me a sort of back-of-the-hand from one reviewer who wanted his science more richly interlarded with exclamation points than I usually see fit to insert. Scientific facts and reasoning are all very well, he seemed to think, but he was anxious to have more gasping and panting, and less cold-blooded explaining.

The way he put it was this: "So while it's nice to have an up-to-date compendium . . . it would have been even nicer to have emerged with at least a whimper of awe and not such a bang of statistics."

There's not much one can do, I suppose, if one happens to be reviewed by someone who's fond of whimpering, but I'm afraid I'm not going to oblige him. It is my firm belief that statistics, properly presented, have within them all the awe anyone needs; and that the Gentle Reader can pick out that awe for himself and doesn't need me to do any whimpering for him.

Anyway—to pick a subject at random—let's consider the two satellites of Mars, and see what the bang of statistics can tell us concerning them.

We'll begin with the matter of distances. Phobos, the closer of Mars' two satellites, is 5700 miles from the center of the planet. Since Mars has a diameter of 4200 miles, its surface is 2100 miles from its center. This means that Phobos is only 3600 miles above the Martian surface. As for Deimos, the farther of the satellites, that is 14,600 miles from Mars' center and 12,500 miles from its surface.

Mars' satellites are much closer to the planetary surface than our Moon is to the Earth. Paradoxically this makes them less easy to see in some ways, for the bulge of Mars' own curvature gets in the way.

The bulge of our own planet does not interfere with the visibility of the Moon. The Moon is so far from us that it can (so to speak) shine over the bulge of the Earth's surface. If our Moon were shining directly over the Earth's equator, it would be visible nearly to the poles. Only within half a degree of either pole would the Moon be below the horizon, hidden by the full extent of Earth's bulge.

But then, the Moon's orbit is tipped 18° with relation to Earth's equator, so that it can shine directly over any latitude from 18° N to 18° S at one time or another. This tilt is more than enough to make the Moon fully visible at either pole. In short, there is no spot on Earth from which the Moon cannot be seen.

The orbits of the Martian satellites, however, are almost exactly in Mars' equatorial plane. Phobos' orbit is tilted to that plane by only 0.95° and Deimos' orbit by 1.3°. This is not enough to overcome the interference of the bulge of Mars' curving surface, to which the Martian satellites are so close.

From any place beyond 83° N or S on the Martian surface, Deimos, the more distant satellite, is never seen. For Phobos, the closer satellite, the situation is even more drastic. Beyond 69° N or S on the Martian surface, Phobos is never seen. This means that from 0.7 percent of the Martian surface one can never see either satellite. From an additional 6 percent of the surface one can see only Deimos, never Phobos.

The two satellites together can be seen only from 92.3 percent of the Martian surface and anyone building tourist resorts on Mars (some day) had better keep this in mind.

Now let's try something else. Phobos makes a full swing about Mars in 7.65 hours; Deimos in 30.3 hours. These are the "sidereal periods"; that is, the time it takes for a satellite to move from a position exactly in line with some particular star, completely around the sky and back to a position exactly in line with that same star.

This period with respect to our own Moon is 27.32 days, yet that is not the length of the month as we ordinarily think of it. What interests us about our Moon's period is its phase changes, and that depends upon its position with respect to the Sun and not with respect to some star. The Moon is "full" when it is exactly on the other side of the Earth from the Sun.

Let us say that when the Moon is "full" it is also immediately in front of a particular star. In 27.32 days it will be in front of that star again, but it will *not* be exactly opposite the Sun this time. In the 27.32 days it has taken the Moon to make its circuit, the Sun will have moved somewhat against the background of the stars as a result of the Earth's revolution about the Sun. It will take additional time for the Moon to make up this added distance and reach the point opposite the Sun again. For that reason the period from full Moon to full Moon is 29.53 days. This is the "synodic month."

It is only fair to ask then if there is an equivalent difference between the sidereal period of Mars' satellites, which is the period usually given, and some synodic period from which we ought to calculate phases.

Well, the size of the difference between the synodic period and the sidereal period depends on how far the planet moves in its revolution about the Sun while the satellite is completing one turn about its orbit.

The closer a planet is to the Sun, the more rapidly it curves about its orbit and the more rapidly the Sun appears to move against the starry background in the planet's skies. On the other hand, the farther the satellite from a planet, the longer it takes to complete an orbital turn and the greater the distance the planet moves about the Sun.

To have a small difference between synodic and sidereal periods, then, you want a planet that is distant from the Sun and a satellite that is close to the planet.

Since Mars is farther from the Sun than the Earth is, and since its satellites are considerably closer to it than the Moon is to the Earth, the difference between synodic and sidereal periods should be much less for Phobos and Deimos, than for the Moon. And this is so.

Where the synodic period of the Moon is 2.2 days longer than its sidereal period, the synodic period of Deimos is only 3.6 *minutes* longer than its sidereal period. This means that Deimos, having made a complete turn about Mars, need only travel an extra 3.6 minutes to catch up with the apparent motion of the Sun in the Martian sky during the interval of the satellite's orbital circle.

Phobos, which is closer to Mars and makes its turn more rapidly, need move only for 14 additional *seconds* to catch up to the Sun. It follows, then, that we can dismiss that particular complication and consider the period of the Martian satellites as, in effect, both sidereal and synodic.

Suppose we were standing on the equator of Mars, and suppose Mars were not rotating but were remaining motionless with respect to the stars. We would see Deimos rise in the west, cross the sky, pass directly overhead, and set in the east.

Does that sound queer? Does it sound odd to talk of rising in the west and setting in the east? That is what would happen under the conditions given, just the same, for Deimos circles Mars west-to-east.

This is the common state of affairs. Phobos circles Mars west-to-east too, and the Moon circles Earth west-to-east. In fact, almost all the satellites circle their planets west-to-east. The few that do not (such as Phoebe, Saturn's outermost satellite) but circle east-to-west, are said to have "retrograde orbits."

Yet if our Moon moves in its orbit west-to-east, why does it rise in the east and set in the west? If it is really moving west-to-east, why does it visibly move east-to-west?

The answer is that we are not standing on a planet that is motionless (as I imagined Mars to be a few paragraphs ago). The Earth is rotating about its axis in a west-to-east direction. (Planets that rotate east-to-west, as Venus does, have "retrograde rotation.")

Earth's rotation carries us west-to-east far more quickly than the Moon's orbital motion carries it west-to-east. Earth makes one complete rotation in 1 day, while the Moon makes one complete orbital revolution in 27.32 days.

As Earth rotates merrily onward, we on its surface overtake the Moon easily and leave it far behind. Of course, we don't sense ourselves moving at all. To ourselves, it seems merely that the Moon is moving backward—that is, from east-to-west. In short the Moon circles the Earth west-to-east relative to Earth's center, but east-to-west relative to a fixed point on Earth's surface.

If the Moon were motionless, Earth's surface would make half its turn in just 12 hours and the Moon would seem to move from Moon-rise in the east to Moon-set in the west in just those 12 hours. However, in those 12 hours, the Moon has moved a little bit west-to-east and the Earth must turn about 25 minutes more to make up for that.

For this reason, there are roughly 12½ hours from Moon-rise to Moon-set and another 12½ hours from Moon-set to the next Moon-rise. This makes about 25 hours from one Moon-rise to the next, which is why the Moon rises one hour later each night. (Actually, this nightly delay in Moon-rise varies through the year because of the eccentricity of the Moon's orbit and of the tilt of its orbital plane, but that need not concern us.)

Let's get back to Deimos. If it circles about Mars in just 30.30 hours, it turns through 360° in that period. In each hour it moves west-to-east through an angle of 11.9°. At the same time, though, Mars is also moving west-to-east in a rotation that takes it 24.62 hours. Mars rotates through an angle of 14.6° in one hour.

The effect of Mars' rotation about its axis, to a person standing on the Martian surface, is to impart an apparent east-to-west motion to Deimos.

Deimos, then, is simultaneously affected by two shifts in position. In one hour, there is an 11.9° shift west-to-east because of its own orbital motion, and a 14.6° shift east-to-west imposed upon it by Mars' rotation. The resultant of these two shifts is that Deimos, as seen from the surface of Mars, moves 2.7° east-to-west in each hour.

In other words, Mars turns a bit faster than Deimos moves, so that the planet's surface overtakes the satellite, but not very rapidly. To an observer on the Martian surface, Deimos therefore seems to move backward (east-to-west) but, as aforesaid, not very rapidly. Indeed, if Deimos moves 2.7° east-to-west, it takes 133 hours to move through 360° and turn completely around Mars relative to a fixed point on its surface.

An observer on the Martian equator would observe Deimos rise in the east, move slowly westward until, after about 33 hours, it would be directly overhead. Another 33 hours would see it set in the west. It would then be fully 66 hours before it would rise again.

Suppose Deimos were a little closer to Mars than it is. It would then move about Mars a little more rapidly west-to-east than it now does. The rotating surface of Mars would overtake it with even greater difficulty so that Deimos would seem to move east-to-west even more slowly.

If Deimos were sufficiently close to Mars, the satellite would turn about Mars west-to-east in exactly the same time it takes Mars to turn about its axis. Satellite and planetary surface would remain neck-and-neck forever. To someone on Mars' equator, Deimos would then seem to remain motionless.

If the observer happened to be on that part of the Martian equator which was directly under Deimos, he would see Deimos directly overhead eternally. If he traveled to other parts of that side of Mars, he would see Deimos lower in the sky in some particular direction. From one half of the Martian surface he would never see Deimos at all; it would be on the opposite side of the planet.

This is what would happen if Deimos were 12,710 miles from the Martian center instead of 14,600 miles. It would then have what is called a "synchronous orbit."

Any planet has a position for a synchronous orbit. Earth's period of rotation is about the same as that of Mars, so you might expect a synchronous orbit in the same position. If so, you'd be wrong. Earth is more massive than Mars and has a stronger gravitational field. It can whip a satellite about itself in 24 hours at a greater distance than Mars can. For Earth such a synchronous orbit would be 26,300 miles from the center of the planet, rather than 12,710 miles.

We have no natural satellite at that distance but we can (and have) put man-made satellites at just that distance. If the orbit of a synchronous satellite is not quite circular, or if it is tilted to the equator, the satellite would seem to oscillate about some central point, in ellipses, figure-eights and so on, but it would never make a complete circle about the planet.

Satellites in synchronous orbit would be of particular use in communications, since one that hovered eternally over the Atlantic Ocean, for instance, would be ever-available for messages back and forth between Europe and the United States.

Let me forestall one inevitable question at this point. Someone is bound to write and ask me how a satellite can hang motionless over a given spot on the Earth without falling.

The answer is that a satellite in synchronous orbit is motionless only with respect to a fixed point on the turning surface of the planet. It is moving rapidly around the planet, relative to the planetary center, and that is what counts.

Now let's pass on to Phobos. Phobos is closer to Mars than Deimos is; quite a bit closer. Phobos therefore moves about Mars west-to-east much more rapidly than Deimos does. In fact, it moves about Mars west-to-east more quickly than Mars rotates west-to-east.

This fact is usually presented in introductory astronomy texts in a kind of breathless fashion, as though it were very odd of Phobos to do this; perhaps even rather talented of it. My friend, the reviewer, might even whimper over it.

Actually, it is not odd at all. It is inevitable! Any satellite will outrace a planetary surface if it is close enough to the planet.

I have already said that if Deimos were 12,710 miles from the center of Mars, it would be in synchronous orbit and would move west-to-east in such a way as to turn about Mars at just the rate that Mars itself turns about its axis. If Deimos were still closer to Mars, it would move still faster and would move about Mars *faster* than Mars moves about its axis.

This is true of *any* satellite that is closer to its planet than the synchronous orbit. The only sizable natural satellite of any planet that happens to have a known orbit closer than synchronous is Phobos. That is what makes Phobos unusual—its closeness to its planet. Once that closeness is granted, the fact that it makes an orbital turn faster than the planet makes an axial turn is inevitable.

Thus, Saturn has a set of rings, the inner portions of which are closer than synchronous. While Saturn rotates on its axis in 10.6 hours, the innermost portions of the ring make turns about Saturn in less time than that.

Again, the distance of our own synchronous orbit is 26,300 miles from Earth's center. Any satellite closer to Earth than that *must* revolve about Earth in less than 24 hours; hence in less time than it takes for Earth to turn on its axis. Most of our artificial satellites are indeed closer than synchronous and therefore do indeed move about the Earth in less than 24 hours. The closest satellites move about the Earth in 1.5 hours.

To be sure, the faster a given planet spins about its axis, the closer to itself is the synchronous orbit. There is no known reason, in theory, why Earth might not rotate in ten hours rather than 24. If it did so, the synchronous orbit would be only 14,600 miles from its center. Indeed, if the Earth rotated about its axis in 1.5 hours, the synchronous orbit would be 4000 miles from its center, or right at its surface.

If Earth rotated about its axis in 1.5 hours, no satellite could possibly turn about the Earth more rapidly than it rotated on its axis. However, when a planet's surface is at synchronous orbit, its equatorial region moves into orbit, if it is not nailed down. (Another way of putting it is that the centrifugal effect would just counterbalance gravitational force.) If Earth rotated on its axis in 1.5 hours, its ocean would be sucked off the surface.

We know of no body that is turning so rapidly as to be coming apart at the equatorial seam, and therefore we know of no body which can't have some satellite closer than synchronous.

But back to Phobos—

It moves about Mars west-to-east in 7.65 hours and therefore covers 47° west-to-east in each hour. Meanwhile, the Martian surface is moving the observer 14.6° west-to-east in each hour. That is not enough to overtake Phobos, but it does cut its speed somewhat. Instead of Phobos moving 47° west-to-east, it moves 32.4° west-to-east in that hour.

But it is still moving *west-to-east.* That means that despite Mars' spin, Phobos rises in the west and sets in the east. Again, this is not clever or perverse of Phobos. It is the inevitable consequence of having an orbit closer than synchronous. All our own artificial satellites (except a small number of really distant ones) rise in the west and set in the east—provided they are hurled into a west-to-east orbit in the first place.

If Phobos moves 32.4° in one hour, it makes a complete turn about Mars, relative to a fixed point on its surface, in 11.1 hours. It rises in the west, is overhead 2.8 hours later, and sets after having been in the sky a total of 5.55 hours.

What's more, every 10.3 hours, Phobos overtakes Deimos and passes within a couple of degrees of it. (Sometimes it must even eclipse Deimos.) While Deimos remains in the Martian sky for a long time, moving slowly east-to-west, Phobos races by six times (sometimes seven) during that interval, making near-contact each time.

But what about the phases of Phobos and Deimos? The full cycle of phases takes place in the course of the satellites' period of revolution relative to the Sun, not relative to a fixed point on the planetary surface.

While it takes Phobos 11.1 hours to circle the Martian sky, it takes it only 7.65 hours to go through its full cycle of phases.

Suppose, for instance, that Phobos rises above the western horizon in the new-Phobos phase. For that to happen, it must rise just as the Sun is setting. (It is not likely to be exactly in front of the Sun, since the Sun's apparent orbit is tipped 24° to that of Phobos and the two may pass each other with quite a gap. This is also true of our own Moon and the Sun, which is why we don't have an eclipse of the Sun every time we have a new Moon—but that's a different subject.)

Anyway, if Phobos rises as the Sun is setting, the satellite rapidly waxes as it rises above the horizon and the Sun moves below it. By the time Phobos has passed the zenith and is halfway down toward the east, it is exactly opposite the Sun, which is now well down Mars' other side, and the satellite is at the full-Phobos phase. When Phobos sets in the east it is in its third quarter and appears as a half-Phobos.

And Deimos? While it remains in the sky 66 hours, it goes through its full cycle of phases in 30.3 hours. If it rises in the east as new-Deimos, it reaches full-Deimos while it is halfway up toward zenith and is new-Deimos again just short of zenith. In fact, it goes through its full set of phases more than twice while it is in the sky. It does this, of course, because Mars' rotation brings the Sun across the sky twice while Deimos is shining there.

So far, things seem pretty exciting. Just imagine two moons of which one stays in the sky practically forever, changing phase as you watch, while the other chases across the sky like a speed-demon—and in the wrong direction, too. And then there is the Sun moving east-to-west over twice as rapidly as Deimos.

But there is one great shortcoming—the size of the satellites.

They are tiny. Deimos is only 6 miles in diameter and Phobos only 10. Even allowing for their closeness to the Martian surface, such bodies can scarcely make an impressive appearance.

For comparison, the Moon's apparent width is 31 minutes of arc. Well, it turns out that Phobos, when directly overhead, at a distance of 3600 miles above the Martian equator, has an apparent width of only 10 minutes of arc; that is, only 1/3 the width of our Moon.

The total apparent area is 1/9 that of the Moon, but it can't be 1/9 as bright as our Moon. It is farther from the Sun and receives less light. It receives only 0.43 times as much light as the Earth-Moon system does and if Phobos is no more efficient than our Moon in reflecting light, then Phobos, when directly overhead, is only 1/20 as bright as our Moon.

As for Deimos, which is smaller than Phobos and more distant, it would appear as a spot of light only 1.6 minutes across. It would look like a fat star about 1/240 as bright (at best) as our full Moon. Its phases would not be visible and it would merely grow dimmer as the Sun drew closer.

That is rather deflationary. Mars' two moons become two small bodies, one no more than a planet-like point and the other a visible globe, but one that is quite small and dim.

Still, let's stop and consider. Even though Deimos is only 1/240 as bright as our full Moon, it would be nearly ten times as bright as Venus (at its brightest) appears to us. It would be a rich and beautiful diamond in the sky, better than anything of the sort we could find in ours.

As for Phobos, that might be a small globe, but it would have certain special points of interest. At the horizon, the observer would be viewing it across Mars' thickness and it would be distinctly farther away than when it was shining directly overhead. When rising, then, Phobos would have an apparent diameter of a little under 6 minutes. As it rises from horizon to zenith, it therefore not only changes phase, but it grows visibly larger, nearly tripling in total area. Then, as it sinks toward the eastern horizon it would grow perceptibly smaller again.

(I wonder if the horizon illusion that makes our own Moon seem so enormous when it is near the horizon would operate on Mars too. It would be a pity, for it might just mask the real change in size of Phobos.)

Take this combination of changing phase and diameter, of wrong-way motion, of constant glancing passages near Deimos, and of frequent dimming as it approaches the Sun and brightening as it leaves it, and Phobos would clearly have an interest and variety our Moon couldn't possibly have, despite its greater size and brightness.

And there's more, too. Phobos is so small that its gravity is not likely to force its substance into a sphere. It can very well have an irregular shape. The asteroid Eros, which is of the same order of magnitude as Phobos, is known to be brick-shaped, for instance.

It might be, then, that Phobos will be seen not as a circle of light, but as an irregular lump upon which the interplay of light and shadow will produce a fascinating display of kaleidoscopic change that will never exhaust the fancy.

That's what the bang of my statistics tells me; *that's* the kind of kaleidoscope in the sky it shows me. If my friend the nameless reviewer reads this, he can whimper in awe if he wishes; I prefer to cheer with delight.

7. THE SYMBOL-MINDED CHEMIST

I view with equanimity the growing numeralization of our society. Calmly I have memorized my zip-code number, my social security number, my area code number, and my all-numeral telephone number. I am even glad that Massachusetts has, for the most part, all-numeral license plates. I have memorized the numbers on both my cars.

I was actually relieved to see letter combinations go. For me, such things are confusing. When I was attending Columbia University, for instance, there were many cars parked in its vicinity with license plates that began with CU. I would pass a car with a license number CU-1234, let us say, and in my mind a maddening little voice would say "copper-1234" because Cu is the chemical symbol for copper.

Here in Newton, the town I live in, we have three telephone exchanges, two of which are Lasell and Bigelow. To me, the number LA5-1234 is "Lanthanum 5-1234" and the number BI4-1234 is "Bismuth 4-1234." Sometimes I ask for telephone numbers in that fashion and produce alarm and despondency in the fair young things at the other end of the wire. (I once asked for a Dewey-2 number, pronouncing it precisely as Dyoo-ee, as is my wont, and the dear young operator asked me, "Is that D-U?")

Well, then, since I am talking about telephone exchanges and chemical symbols, and since telephone exchanges are disappearing, let's concentrate on chemical symbols. (How's that for sneakiness?)

I strongly suspect that the advance of science or any branch of it depends upon the development of a simple and standardized language into which its concepts can be put. Only in this manner can one scientist understand another in his field. Without it, communication breaks down and, as a result, everything else does too.

Prior to the eighteenth century, for instance, there was no generally agreed-upon chemical language. On the contrary, alchemists gloried in obscurity and made up the most fanciful appellations for the various substances they worked with. Using mythology and metaphor they strove to make themselves sound mystical and great and to obscure the fact that, in general, they didn't know what they were talking about. (There were honorable exceptions, of course.)

The result was that when serious chemists arose, they found they could not understand the work of the past (and among the alchemical fakery and nonsense were hidden some real and important achievements it would have been important to unearth). They could scarcely understand each other, in fact, and chemistry could advance only with difficulty, if at all.

Toward the end of the eighteenth century, chemists were painfully aware of the language difficulty and in 1782 the French chemist Louis Bernard Guyton de Morveau published a paper pointing out the need for a systematized, simple, and logical chemical nomenclature.

This caught the eye of Antoine Laurent Lavoisier, the foremost chemist of the time. He joined with Guyton de Morveau and with two other chemists, Claude Louis Berthollet and Antoine François de Fourcroy, to work out such a language, and by 1787 this was done.

It is the chemical language we still use today. When we speak of "sodium chloride" or "sulfuric acid" or "potassium periodate" we are using the language worked out by Lavoisier and the rest, and it works fine.

At least it works fine for inorganic compounds which have relatively simple compositions. Organic compounds (those containing carbon and hydrogen atoms) are another matter entirely. They proved to be entirely too complicated for Lavoisier's simple language.

Organic nomenclature grew almost haphazardly and was filled with "trivial names" (names that are made up without any reference to—or, sometimes, knowledge of—the constitution of the compound), most of which can't be gotten rid of now. It was not until 1892 that, at an International Congress of chemists held in Geneva, a systematic system of nomenclature for organic compounds was worked out, a nomenclature that could be used to write the molecular structure of any compound named.

For instance, if someone gives me the name "9, 12, 15-octadecatrienoic acid" I can write the formula of that compound, since I happen to know the Geneva nomenclature; and I can do so even if I have never heard of that particular compound before. If I am, however, given the equivalent trivial name of the compound—that is, linolenic acid—then I am helpless. Either I happen to know the formula or I am stuck.

Still, while words are useful and even satisfactory for inorganic compounds and for organic compounds that are not *too* complicated, they are not the ultimate. Something still simpler than words, and something capable of more graphic combination to show molecular structure, is needed.

The first opportunity to pass beyond words came in the opening decade of the nineteenth century, when the English chemist John Dalton worked out the modern atomic theory. Dalton suggested that all matter was made up of atoms, that each element was made up of a distinct species of atom, and that materials that were not elements were composed of atoms of different elements in close association. Why, then, should we not represent each different kind of atom or element with some sort of symbol? The structure of compounds (substances that are not elements) can then be shown by putting together the symbols of different atoms in appropriate combination to form what eventually came to be called molecules.

In 1808 Dalton published his symbols. Each atom was a little circle, naturally, and different atoms were distinguished by small variations among the circles. An unadorned circle represented an oxygen atom; a circle with a dot in the middle was a hydrogen atom; a circle with a vertical line dividing it into equal halves was a nitrogen atom; a circle that was blacked in completely was a carbon atom, and so on.

These circles looked very graphic, but they were "trivial." Nothing about them necessarily suggested which element they represented (although the black circle did suggest the blackness of carbon). They had to be memorized.

What's more, although the number of elements known in 1808 was far smaller than those known today, there were still too many to be conveniently represented by sheer geometry. Dalton found himself forced to use initials. The sulfur atom was represented by a circle with an "S" inside, the phosphorus atom by a circle with a "P" inside, and so on.

The Swedish chemist Jöns Jakob Berzelius, went a step further in 1814. Why bother with circles if one had to place initials inside? Surely the initials were sufficient in themselves. S and P could stand for sulfur and phosphorus, respectively, without the frippery of an enclosing circle.

As far as possible, Berzelius suggested, each element ought to be represented by its initial. If more than one element began with the same letter, one could be represented by the initial and the rest by the initial plus a second letter distinctive enough to suggest the name of the element. Thus, if carbon is represented as C, then chlorine can be represented as Cl, chromium as Cr, and cobalt as Co.

Berzelius's system was adopted almost at once, remains in force to the present day, and will probably never be changed. The letter or letters representing the element in general (or a single atom of that element in particular) are known as the "chemical symbol" of that element, and to any professional chemist they become so familiar that, as in my case, telephone exchanges and automobile licenses become elements.

It is a sad commentary on human nature that John Dalton, a gentle Quaker, a noble character, and a great man of science, could not bring himself to accept what the rest of the world, then and since, agreed was an improvement on his own suggestion. To Dalton, Berzelius's system was no more than an alphabet soup which he felt sure would not establish itself. He was wrong.

Berzelius had a rather complicated system for envisaging the manner in which these chemical symbols of the elements could be put together to suggest molecular structure. That part of his system was abandoned in favor of the use of numbers. Thus, if the water molecule contains two hydrogen atoms and one oxygen atom, it is H_2O; if the sulfuric acid molecule contains two hydrogen atoms, a sulfur atom, and four oxygen atoms, it is H_2SO_4, and so on.

Such a system is quite satisfactory for most inorganic compounds and a few organic ones. However, in organic chemistry, all but a very few kinds of molecules have such complicated structures that a mere enumeration of atoms is insufficient. Special "structural formulas" had to be invented, but that is another story.

Suppose, then, that we concentrate only on the chemical symbols of the elements themselves for the rest of the article, and forget about molecules. Ideally, there should be only initials, but there are only 26 letters to the alphabet and there are more than 26 different elements.

In fact, there are 104 elements known at present. Of these, the 104th has recently been discovered by Soviet scientists and has not yet been given a name and a symbol. Still that leaves 103 elements with names and symbols, so chemists are forced, whether they will or no, into two-letter symbols. Fortunately, nothing more is needed. There are 26×26 or 676 different two-letter combinations and we are not likely ever to reach that number of elements.

In fact, when later chemists considered the matter, they were sorry that single letters had ever been used for symbols. It was neater to be uniform and since it was impossible to give every element a one-letter symbol, it would have been desirable to give every element, without exception, a two-letter symbol. For that reason chemists have, in the last century, usually given new elements two-letter symbols even when a one-letter symbol was available.

Those elements that are now represented by a single letter were, in almost every case, known at the time that Berzelius was establishing his system and they received their symbols then. The initial letters were then frozen into chemical history and, in almost every case, could no longer be changed. So many thousands of papers and books have referred to the oxygen atom as O so many millions of times that to begin to refer to the oxygen atom as Ox, for instance, is now unthinkable.

Sixteen elements are symbolized (or have been symbolized) by single letters. Let's list them in Table 6, in the order of discovery:

TABLE 6: SINGLE-LETTER SYMBOLS

Element	*Symbol*	*Year of Discovery*
Carbon	C	prehistoric
Sulfur	S	prehistoric
Phosphorus	P	1669
Nitrogen	N	1772
Oxygen	O	1774
Tungsten	W	1783
Uranium	U	1789
Hydrogen	H	1790
Yttrium	Y	1794
Potassium	K	1807
Boron	B	1808
Iodine	I	1811
Vanadium	V	1830
Fluorine	F	1886
Argon	A	1894
Einsteinium	E	1952

Of these sixteen, twelve were known at the time that Berzelius first advanced his system, and vanadium was discovered while the system was still young. One-letter symbols were viewed favorably then. Fluorine was not isolated till 1886, but its existence was known in Berzelius's time. It had been named then and had received its symbol.

Only two elements discovered after 1830, without prior suspicion of their existence, were given single-letter symbols. These were argon and einsteinium and, as it happened, neither kept those symbols.

In 1957 an official body of chemists made some recommendations as to chemical symbols which were adopted. They would gladly, I suspect, have wiped out all one-letter symbols, but they couldn't. However, they could forbid one-letter symbols in the future and they could tackle argon and einsteinium. Argon forms no known compounds so that its symbol is rarely used in chemical papers, and einsteinium had only been known for five years and that in the barest submicroscopic traces so that its compounds had not been studied. Therefore, it was safe to decree that the symbol for argon would be, henceforth, Ar instead of A, and the symbol for einsteinium would be Es instead of E.

Looking at Table 6, you can see that two of the symbols do not appear to be true initials. The symbol for tungsten is W and that for potassium is K. Why is that?

The answer is that while in modern times names given to new elements are accepted internationally (with minor inflectional differences) this is not true of elements known from ancient times. What we call iron in English is "Eisen" in German, "fer" in French, and "hierro" in Spanish. Well, then, if we use initials, should the symbol for the element be I, E, F, or H.

Berzelius's decision (a wise one) was to favor no living nation and to use the Latin names of all elements, where those existed. Well, eight of the elements discovered before the custom of uniform international usage was established have names that are distinctly different in English and in Latin. Three others are different in English and in German and international usage has fixed on the German names for the symbols. All eleven are listed in alphabetical order in Table 7:

TABLE 7: NAMES OF ELEMENTS

English name	*Latin name*	*Symbol*
Antimony	Stibium	Sb
Copper	Cuprum	Cu
Gold	Aurum	Au
Iron	Ferrum	Fe
Lead	Plumbum	Pb
Mercury	Hydrargyrum	Hg
Potassium	Kalium*	K
Silver	Argentum	Ag
Sodium	Natrium*	Na
Tin	Stannum	Sn
Tungsten	Wolfram*	W

* German usage

Some of these various names can be traced. "Cuprum" is supposed to be derived from the island of Cyprus (Kupros, in Greek) where copper mines were found in early ancient times; and from "cuprum" comes "copper."

"Hydrargyrum" means "water-silver" or "liquid silver," which is an apt description of the element we know as mercury. The old English name "quicksilver" is similar. "Quick" means "alive" (as in "the quick and the dead") and quicksilver darts here and there like a living thing when spilled, instead of sitting like a lump of ordinary dead silver.

The name "mercury" dates back to the Middle Ages, when the alchemists lined up the seven metals with the seven planets. Gold was the Sun, silver was the Moon, and copper was Venus—the three most precious metals lined up with the three most brilliant planets in order of preciousness and of brilliance. (The Sun and the Moon were considered planets in the days before Copernicus.) Iron was Mars because iron is characteristic of the weapons of war; quicksilver was Mercury because Mercury moved so quickly through the heavens, like darting quicksilver; and lead was Saturn, because Saturn moved more slowly than any other planet and therefore seemed leaden in its motions. Tin was Jupiter by elimination. Of these names, only Mercury maintained its identification, and what was quicksilver became mercury.

The remaining Latin names: aurum, ferrum, plumbum, argentum, and stannum, are of uncertain origin. Of the English names, "tin" may possibly have come from "stannum"; "iron" may come from the same source as "ore"; and "gold" may be derived from an old Teutonic word for "yellow" (even today the German word for yellow is "gelb"). The words "lead" and "silver" are of uncertain origin.

Antimony was discovered about 1450. Why it should be called antimony is unknown, and most derivations I have seen for it are completely unconvincing. Although the metal itself was not known in ancient times, certain of its compounds, in powdered form, were used to darken the eyelids (a kind of primitive mascara) and the Latin name "stibium" may come from a word meaning "mark." One of the suggested derivations for "antimony" tries to obtain it from "stibium" by way of the Arabic.

Tungsten occurs in a mineral found in Germany called "wolframite," a name of uncertain origin. It also occurs in a mineral found in Sweden and called "tungsten" (meaning "heavy stone" in Swedish, because the mineral happens to be markedly denser than ordinary rocks). The metal occurring in these minerals was isolated, nearly simultaneously, in Sweden and in Germany; in Sweden by Karl Wilhelm Scheele and in Germany by two Spanish brothers, Fausto and Juan José de Elhuyar. Scheele called the metal "tungsten" after the mineral, while the mineral was eventually given the new name of "scheelite" in Scheele's honor. The Elhuyar brothers named the metal "wolfram," from the mineral. In English, tungsten came into use, but international usage drew the chemical symbol for the element from wolfram.

There is an element that can be isolated from a compound known as "soda niter." In 1807 the English chemist Humphry

Davy isolated it from another compound called simply "soda" and he named it "sodium" in consequence. The Germans, however, preferred to concentrate on the "niter" and they named it "Natrium." International usage settled on the Natrium for the symbol. Another element found in soda niter came to be called "nitrogen" in English, so that "nitrogen" and "Natrium" are, in essence, the same word, although they describe two entirely different elements.

In ancient times, a useful chemical was obtained by burning certain plants in large pots and leaching the ashes with water. In English the resulting compound, in very straightforward fashion, was called "pot ash" which was eventually run into a single word —potash.

In Arabic, however, the substance was "al-kili," meaning "the ash." The substance is what chemists would nowadays call a fairly strong base and such substances are now called "alkalis"—from the Arabic.

A metal was isolated by Humphry Davy in 1807 from potash, and he named it "potassium." The German chemists, however, preferred to go to the Arabic and from al-kili came "Kalium." It was the latter from which the chemical symbol was drawn.

You mustn't think, though, that German youngsters studying chemistry have it better than we do because Na, K, and W make immediate sense to them and not to us.

The Germans, generally, are more reluctant to make use of Greek and Latin words in forming their own terms, but stick to German. We have hydrogen ("water-producer"), oxygen ("acid-producer"), and nitrogen ("niter-producer") as three very common and important elements—with names derived from the Greek.

The German equivalents, in down-to-Earth German, are Wasserstoff ("water-substance"), Sauerstoff ("acid-substance"), and Stickstoff ("suffocation-substance"). Pity the poor German youngsters taking their first chemistry courses and wondering why

Wasserstoff should be symbolized as H, Sauerstoff as O, and Stickstoff as N. For, of course, the Germans use the international symbols as all other nations do.

To professional chemists, these anomalies offer no problem. The symbols become second-nature, take my word for it, and "Na" becomes "sodium" so firmly that a chemist would face the symbol "So" in complete confusion and find himself unable to imagine what element that could possibly represent.

To the beginner, though, the Na/sodium relationship is a puzzle, and even less peculiar symbols aren't clear. For instance, is Cl chlorine or calcium, is Ca calcium or californium, is Th thorium, thulium, or thallium, is Ni nickel or nitrogen, is As arsenic or astatine, is Ir iron or iridium and so on.

If such a beginner is presented with a periodic table of the elements, he has to run up and down it in a hit-and-miss way seeking for the symbol whose element he is trying to identify. If he has an alphabetic listing of the elements, that makes things a little easier for the symbols are then roughly in alphabetic order, but not exactly. There still has to be some hunting.

What the first-year chemistry student really needs is an alphabetical listing of *symbols* as in Table 8:

TABLE 8: CHEMICAL SYMBOLS ARRANGED ALPHABETICALLY

Chemical Symbol	*Element*	*Chemical Symbol*	*Element*
Ac	Actinium	Br	Bromine
Ag	Silver (Argentum)	C	Carbon
Al	Aluminum	Ca	Calcium
Am	Americium	Cd	Cadmium
Ar	Argon	Ce	Cerium
As	Arsenic	Cf	Californium
At	Astatine	Cl	Chlorine
Au	Gold (Aurum)	Cm	Curium
B	Boron	Co	Cobalt
Ba	Barium	Cr	Chromium
Bi	Beryllium	Cs	Cesium
Be	Bismuth	Cu	Copper (Cuprum)
Bk	Berkelium	Dy	Dysprosium

Chemical Symbol	*Element*	*Chemical Symbol*	*Element*
Er	Erbium	P	Phosphorus
Es	Einsteinium	Pa	Protactinium
Eu	Europium	Pb	Lead (Plumbum)
F	Fluorine	Pd	Palladium
Fe	Iron (Ferrum)	Pm	Promethium
Fm	Fermium	Po	Polonium
Fr	Francium	Pr	Praseodymium
Ga	Gallium	Pt	Platinum
Gd	Gadolinium	Pu	Plutonium
Ge	Germanium	Ra	Radium
H	Hydrogen	Rb	Rubidium
He	Helium	Re	Rhenium
Hf	Hafnium	Rh	Rhodium
Hg	Mercury (Hydrargyrum)	Rn	Radon
		Ru	Ruthenium
Ho	Holmium	S	Sulfur
I	Iodine	Sb	Antimony (Stibium)
In	Indium	Sc	Scandium
Ir	Iridium	Se	Selenium
K	Potassium (Kalium)	Si	Silicon
Kr	Krypton	Sm	Samarium
La	Lanthanum	Sn	Tin (Stannum)
Li	Lithium	Sr	Strontium
Lr	Lawrencium	Ta	Tantalum
Lu	Lutetium	Tb	Terbium
Md	Mendelevium	Tc	Technetium
Mg	Magnesium	Te	Tellurium
Mn	Manganese	Th	Thorium
Mo	Molybdenum	Ti	Titanium
N	Nitrogen	Tl	Thallium
Na	Sodium (Natrium)	Tm	Thulium
Nb	Niobium	U	Uranium
Nd	Neodymium	V	Vanadium
Ne	Neon	W	Tungsten (Wolfram)
Ni	Nickel	Xe	Xenon
No	Nobelium	Y	Yttrium
Np	Neptunium	Yb	Ytterbium
O	Oxygen	Zn	Zinc
Os	Osmium	Zr	Zirconium

Some final notes. The element niobium is known quite commonly as "columbium," particularly in the United States. The element under that alias has the symbol Cb. Nobelium, on the other hand, had no official name for a while. The initial discoverers, who gave it its name, described an experiment that couldn't be repeated. The element was discovered later by another type of experiment that could be repeated. The second discoverers could, if they chose, give the element another name, but in 1967 they decided to go along with nobelium. Again, lawrencium was given the symbol Lw when it was first isolated in 1961, but this was changed to Lr in 1963.

Finally, the Soviet chemists have not yet named element 104 but there are rumors that they may name it in honor of Igor Vasilevich Kurchatov, who died in 1960. He had led the Soviet team that developed nuclear bombs after World War II. If so, element 104 will probably be called "kurchatovium" and its symbol will probably be Kc.

8. THE GREAT BORNING

Back in 1950 Immanuel Velikovsky published a book called *Worlds in Collision* that was a nine-day wonder. For a while, it ranked with flying saucers as a topic of conversation, while orthodox astronomers foamed at the mouth.

Velikovsky, you see, felt that Venus was a late acquisition of the Solar system. A little over three thousand years ago (he maintained) it was spewed out by Jupiter. It sailed through the inner Solar system, spending some time quite close to Earth, and, eventually, settled down in its present orbit.

The close approach of Venus and Earth brought about a series of catastrophes which were recorded in the Bible—according to Velikovsky—as the Egyptian plagues that accompanied the Israelite Exodus. Velikovsky also felt that it was Venus's influence that stopped the Earth's rotation for a bit, and that this is mentioned in the Bible at the point where the Sun and Moon paused in the sky in order that Joshua might win a battle.

Of course, I didn't take *Worlds in Collision* seriously for a moment (even though it is fascinating reading). What edged my skepticism most was the thought of Earth experiencing so drastic an event as the halting of its rotation with so little consequence. Life seemed to continue right through and civilizations were not even disrupted. Despite Velikovsky's talk about legends and vague poetical passages in the psalms there are no clear references in historic annals to any odd astronomical manifestations about

1200 B.C. The oddest point of all is that Joshua's army watched the Sun and Moon come to a halt and, despite the fact that this meant Earth's rotation had ceased, never even fell off their feet. They would have done so if a bus had braked suddenly!

One cannot get from *Worlds in Collision* an adequate picture of what catastrophe on an astronomic scale *really* is.

It was with a certain grim pleasure, therefore, that I discovered a description of a possible astronomic event very much like that postulated by Velikovsky, but with much more realistic consequences.

In order to lay the background properly, however, we must go back to an English surveyor, William Smith, in the closing years of the eighteenth century. In those years, England was interlacing itself with canals, since the railroad had not yet been invented, and Smith was employed in connection with some of the construction. At excavation sites he could not help but notice the manner in which different kinds of rocks were arranged in parallel layers, or "strata."

Others had observed this, too, but Smith went further. He noted that each stratum had its particular types of fossils and maintained that particular strata could be identified by their fossil content even though geological processes had bent, twisted, eroded and otherwise interrupted the smooth continuity that must have existed originally. Smith made this important point in a book published in 1816.

It had always seemed reasonable that in any one place, those strata of rock that were deeper under the surface were also older. Now, however, it became possible to correlate the strata in one place with those in a far distant place by fossil content. The science of "stratigraphy" was born.

In the eighteenth century, early geologists had already decided that the strata could be divided into three broad groups. The lowermost and oldest was known as the Primary; above it was the Secondary, and higher still was the Tertiary. That was as straightforward, surely, as one, two, three. (In 1829 a fourth division, more recent than any of the others, and, indeed, virtually contemporary in comparison, was named, inevitably, Quaternary.)

The division, however, was not very useful, for one could not always tell from geological considerations alone whether strata were Primary, Secondary, or Tertiary. The processes of mountain-building and erosion badly jumbled the layers. By using the fossil content as the key, however, all became clear (well, nearly all) and so it was only right that the strata receive new names referring to the fossils.

This was carried through by a group of British geologists who dominated the early "heroic age" of the science.

One of them, Adam Sedgwick (under whom Charles Darwin studied), suggested the name "Paleozoic" for the Primary strata, and "Cenozoic" for the Tertiary plus Quaternary strata. These are from Greek words meaning "ancient life" and "recent life" respectively.

Another English geologist, John Phillips, a nephew of William Smith, rushed in with Mesozoic ("middle life") for the Secondary strata.

These broad-beamed divisions are the geological eras and we therefore have, reading from old to recent, the Paleozoic Era, the Mesozoic Era, and the Cenozoic Era.

The division is particularly neat from the standpoint of evolution, as is to be expected since it was built up out of the consideration of fossils. The Paleozoic was the great age of the fish for the dry land was barren at its start and was just being colonized in its later stages. In the Mesozoic, the dry land was fully conquered and it was the heyday of the reptiles—the time of the dinosaurs. Finally, the Cenozoic represents the age of the mammals and we still live in the Cenozoic today.

Naturally, as the strata were studied more carefully, it became possible to divide each era into periods, each period into epochs, each epoch into ages, and so on. However, I won't delve into more than a few of the divisions.

The periods of an era (and the finer divisions also) were often named after the region in which the strata studied were of the type that were sufficiently undisturbed to allow the distinctions to be made. Since British geologists dominated the science in the generation following Smith, many of the place names are to be found in Great Britain.

Thus, the Paleozoic Era was eventually divided into six periods which, in order of decreasing age, are: Cambrian, Ordovician, Silurian, Devonian, Carboniferous, and Permian. Of these, four memorialize British regions.

Indeed the only period of the Paleozoic that does not refer to a region is the Carboniferous. That was the first to be named, in 1822, by two Englishmen, the aforementioned John Phillips, together with William Daniel Conybeare. They introduced the term before the habit of naming for regions had been set.

The name is all the better for that, since it describes an important characteristic of the period. The name means "coal-producing" and it is the Carboniferous strata that contain the great coal seams. The Carboniferous period is, however, divided into two epochs which I shall name because they represent American regions and were introduced by American geologists. The earlier is the Mississippian (named for the river, not the state, and originating out of investigations in Illinois and Iowa) and the later is the Pennsylvanian.

You may be wondering by now which four represent British regions, and you may not be at all helped if I tell you that three involve Wales. If so, that is because you are not taking into account the determined classicism of the nineteenth-century British scholars.

Sedgwick was studying the strata in parts of Wales and, in 1835, suggested the earliest rocks of the Paleozoic be named for that nation. But he used the Latin name, Cambria, and thus we now speak of the Cambrian period.

Still another British geologist, Sir Roderick Impey Murchison, also investigated the rocks of Wales and, in 1839, published his results. He named his period after the Silures, a tribe of Britons who had once inhabited South Wales and who are mentioned in Caesar's Commentaries.

This particular tribe appealed to British pride, for they had resisted the Roman invasion strongly. Their leader, Caractacus, had fought off the Romans for years until finally captured in A.D. 50. (Gilbert and Sullivan enthusiasts must already be thinking that the modern Major General boasted he could "tell you every detail of Caractacus's uniform"—yes, *that* Caractacus.) Anyway, Murchison's strata are now known as belonging to the Silurian period.

In that same year, Murchison and Sedgwick, in collaboration, studied the rock structure in Devon, an English shire just south of Wales across the Bristol channel. Those strata came to represent the Devonian period.

Finally forty years later, in 1879, another English geologist, Charles Lapworth, managed to distinguish a group of strata that included the latest Cambrian and earliest Silurian, as previously defined. He demonstrated these strata to deserve a period to themselves and it became the Ordovician period. Whereas the Silurian had been named for a tribe in south Wales, the Ordovician was named, symmetrically enough, for the Ordovices, a contemporary tribe in north Wales.

The sixth period of the Paleozoic is the only one to call in a region outside Great Britain. It is the Permian period and it is named for Perm, a city in the Urals, deep within Russia and on the border of Siberia. How on Earth, you must wonder, did the Russians intrude into the British preserves of the Paleozoic?

They didn't. It was rather the other way around. Murchison, having nosed his way across Wales and Devon, came to head a geological survey into the Urals and it was he who continued the regional naming habit even in darkest Russia.

The Mesozoic Era is divided into three periods, which in order of decreasing age are the Triassic, the Jurassic, and the Cretaceous, and for these names we must thank the Germans and French.

The third and youngest of these periods was the earliest named.

Like the Carboniferous, it was named in 1822 well before the regional habit began. Like the Carboniferous, too, the Cretaceous was named for its contents. The French geologist Omalius d'Halloy found the deposits he was studying to contain a high chalk content and he therefore named them as belonging to the Cretaceous period (from a Greek word meaning "chalky"). The famous white chalk cliffs of Dover are Cretaceous rock, for instance.

In 1829, however, another French geologist, Alexandre Brogniart, was studying strata that were earlier than the Cretaceous. He was working in the Jura Mountains on the French-Swiss border and it seemed the most natural thing in the world to speak of the Jurassic period.

In 1834 a German geologist, Friedrich August von Alberti, was studying still earlier strata which, it seemed to him, were easily divisible into three layers. From the Greek word for "three" and influenced by the earlier name "Jurassic," the term Triassic period was introduced by Von Alberti.

The Cenozoic Era is divided into two periods, which keep their older-fashioned names, the Tertiary and the Quaternary. The former is divided into five epochs with a beautiful set of repetitive names: Paleocene, Eocene, Oligocene, Miocene, and Pliocene* in order of decreasing age.

Three of these names were introduced by the British geologist Sir Charles Lyell in 1833. These were the Eocene, Miocene, and Pliocene. Their meanings, from the Greek, might be given, rather freely, as "the beginning of the recent," "a bit of the recent," and "more of the recent."

In 1854, however, the German geologist Heinrich Ernst Beyrich decided the section between the Eocene and Miocene deserved an epoch all its own. He kept to the pattern by calling it the Oligocene ("a little bit of the recent").

So did the German botanist Wilhelm Philipp Schimper, who,

* I sometimes wonder how long it will be before some geologist, delivering a popular lecture, will rattle off these names and then add, straight-faced, "And then, of course, we have the modern, or Obscene, epoch."

in 1874, decided that the plant fossils in the earliest Eocene were sufficiently distinct to deserve an epoch of their own. He introduced the Paleocene ("the very beginning of the recent").

The Quaternary period is almost entirely a single epoch, which fits prettily into the epochs of the Tertiary. It is the Pleistocene, a term introduced by Lyell (which is why it fits) and it means "most recent."

But Lyell also gave a name to the final epoch, dating from the end of the Ice Age, and therefore only a few thousand years old, so far. Abandoning all Greek, he called it simply, Recent.

There is the list of the eras and the epochs, which must not be taken as marked off distinctly in the rocks. They are man-made divisions and melt into each other more or less gradually. The disappearance of some types of fossils and the appearance of others mark the division but there are always numerous types of fossils that march across the dividing line.

The sharpest recent dividing line is that marking the end of the Cretaceous and the beginning of the Tertiary. It was a time of a "Great Dying" as all the various groups of dinosaurs and related reptiles perished, both in the sea and on land. Over a very short time, geologically speaking, there was a complete revolution and, where reptiles had been supreme, a suddenly expanding mammalian order dominated the land.

So sudden was the changeover that reasons have desperately been sought to account for it. Men have offered climatic changes, mountain-building, parasite diseases, all sorts of things, to account for it, but the solution is not yet.

The sharp ending of the Cretaceous is, however, only the second most remarkable dividing line in geological history. The most remarkable is the beginning of the Cambrian some 600 million years ago. That was a time of a "Great Borning" (or whatever the opposite of "Great Dying" might be).

Rocks that are older than the Cambrian contain no fossils while the Cambrian rocks swarm with them. Over a relatively short period of time, geologically speaking, life appeared in great variety, with representatives of every modern phylum except Chordata (the one to which we belong) in evidence.

One might argue that it was shortly before the opening of the Cambrian that life developed, and that the geological record merely marks the beginning of life. If this were so, then life would be a recent phenomenon indeed. The rocks that must have seemed terribly ancient to Sedgwick, Murchison, and company, have been found to be far more ancient than they thought, but they still stretch back only some 600 million years and that is not much in the lifetime of an Earth that is at least 4700 million years old. Life would then have occupied Earth only during the final eighth of its history.

Because of the absence of fossils, it is difficult to do anything much about rocks older than the Cambrian and the entire seven-eighths of Earth's history before that time is sometimes called simply the pre-Cambrian era.

Yet there is something funny here. The Cambrian is *too* rich in life and the life-forms are too advanced. It is inconceivable that there wasn't a long evolutionary history behind the complex trilobites that dominate the Cambrian oceans.

Furthermore, there *are* faint traces of life in rocks that are as much as 3000 million years old. No more, admittedly, than carbon deposits that might have originated from algae, but life is life. For that reason, geologists have taken to lumping the eras into still larger divisions called eons.

Everything from the beginning of the Cambrian makes up the Phanerozoic eon ("visible life"). Everything pre-Cambrian makes up the Cryptozoic eon ("hidden life"). Indeed, the pre-Cambrian is now divided into two eras. Those strata in which the earliest algae traces are found are said to belong to the Archeozoic era ("ancient life"). The later pre-Cambrian is the Proterozoic era ("early life").

Now we can summarize the names of the geological divisions mentioned in this article in Table 9:

TABLE 9—THE GEOLOGICAL DIVISIONS

Eons	*Eras*	*Periods*	*Epochs*
Phanerozoic	Cenozoic	Quaternary	Recent
			Pleistocene
		Tertiary	Pliocene
			Miocene
			Oligocene
			Eocene
			Paleocene
	Mesozoic	Cretaceous	
		Jurassic	
		Triassic	
	Paleozoic	Permian	
		Carboniferous	Pennsylvanian
			Mississippian
		Devonian	
		Silurian	
		Ordovician	
		Cambrian	
Cryptozoic (or pre-Cambrian)	Proterozoic		
	Archeozoic		

It would seem, then, that the opening of the Cambrian marks not so much the beginning of life, but the rather sudden increase in complexity of life. What had previously been a system of soft-celled (perhaps microscopic) forms incapable of leaving a fossil record, suddenly became a variegated display of creatures with shells and armor, well designed for preservation.

But why? Why, after a couple of billion years of soft cell life did Earth's life-forms suddenly swell and flourish into a mighty stream of complexity? Two possible answers appeal to me; one chemical and one astronomical.

Sometime before the opening of the Cambrian period—to take the chemical explanation first—photosynthesis had been developed. Where previously the ultimate source of life-energy had been the Sun's ultraviolet, which slowly built up complicated compounds in the ocean, the new photosynthesizing cells could make use of the visible light of the Sun. The Sun's radiation was richer in visible light than in ultraviolet and the photosynthesizing cells flourished.

In the process of photosynthesis, oxygen was produced. This first consumed the reducing compounds of the atmosphere and then began to accumulate there as free oxygen.

Animal life developed which was capable of making use of the free oxygen that was suddenly to be found in the atmosphere and dissolved in the ocean water. Reactions making use of free oxygen liberate some twenty times more energy per glucose molecule than do reactions not involving oxygen. Life found at its disposal a flood of energy in unprecedented quantity.

This did not happen all at once. The oxygen content of Earth's atmosphere rose slowly. By the opening of the Cambrian, it is estimated that oxygen made up two percent of the air; that is, a tenth of the concentration now present. This marked a critical point, perhaps, a point at which oxygen-using reactions became practical and the tidal wave of energy began to pour in.

The Cambrian, then, would mark the moment when life grew

rich and luxurious, expanding in quantity, variety, and complexity, out of what might almost be considered the sheer exuberance of being able to breathe.

The chemical explanation does not account for something else, however. The beginning of the Cambrian is marked by more than the transition to fossils. It is preceded by a period of strong erosion that may have lasted for 100 million years. The continents were ground down to virtual flatness. Neither before nor since, as far as we can tell, was the Earth's surface so generally low-lying and smooth.

Something seems to have gone over the Earth like a grindstone. The easiest explanation is that Earth had experienced a gigantic glacial period and that it had been the creeping glaciers that had smoothed the continents. Opposed to that, however, are certain chemical characteristics of the rocks of the period which seem to imply that this period in geological history was rather warm and could not have been glacial.

So we turn to the astronomical theory to account for this sharp geological boundary before the Cambrian (such a boundary is called an "unconformity").

The interesting possibility is now being bruited about that the Moon became associated with ourselves not in the early dawn of the history of the Solar system, but comparatively recently.

Not recently, you understand in Velikovskian terms, but recently enough. The suggestion is that the Moon was captured by the Earth about 1000 million years ago and that the Earth, for about three-quarters of its history had, like Venus, been without a satellite. (Where the Moon came from and what it was doing before it was captured remains an open question.)

At least one set of calculations shows that the Moon must have been moving in a retrograde orbit when it was captured (a direction opposite to that in which it now moves). In such a case, tidal action acts to bring the Moon closer and closer to Earth (as Neptune's satellite, Triton, is, under similar conditions, being brought closer and closer to Neptune). After a certain point, the orbit is (in gradual stages) reversed and the Moon begins to recede again, eventually reaching its present distance.

The point of closest approach, during the 100 million years prior to the Cambrian, may have been not more than 11,500 miles from the surface of the Earth.

The Moon would then have been a terrific sight indeed. It would have been 10.8° in diameter and therefore 21 times as wide as the Moon appears now. It would have had 440 times the area and would therefore have been 440 times as bright.

But don't fall in love with the thought of our glorious pre-Cambrian satellite. In addition to beauty and brilliance, the nearby Moon produced tides—and what tides!

Let me at this point quote from an article in *American Scientist*, volume 54, page 458, entitled "Origin of the Cambrian-Precambrian Unconformity" and written by Walter S. Olson.

He says, "At that time the tides were 8000 times higher than at present, attaining amplitudes comparable with the present mean ocean depth." In other words, virtually the entire ocean was sloshed over the continents.

Olson goes on to say, "Anyone who has seen the effects of storm tides on the shore line will have a faint idea of the effect of tides with amplitudes of thousands of feet. The tides would eventually sweep across the interior and, laden with sediment and rock fragments, abrade the land surface and reduce the continents to peneplains. The detritus would fill any existing deep basins and be swept over the edges of the continental shelves and dumped into the oceans."

In other words, the Earth's surface would be sandpapered down to flatness while the oceans were filled to shallowness.

But Earth must have been bearing life at this time. Would it have survived? Obviously it did survive. The polar oceans would be relatively little affected by the tides and in it life must have held on grimly.

It may even have been that fairly complex life-forms survived through this watery madness and served to give the Cambrian a good headstart, thus making it unnecessary to suppose the first fossils developed from scratch.

You might wonder why, if the period of Moon-madness contained complex life-forms, there was no evidence of it in the rocks. Ah—that's where the astronomical explanation is so handy. The abrasion of the tides would clearly have wiped the continents clean of all fossil-bearing rocks. The record of the rocks was erased and all we can possibly learn is what followed since.

For all we know, if this theory is correct, there might have been land-life in the pre-Cambrian. It would have been completely wiped out by the tides, leaving not a trace behind. Sea-life would have had to begin all over and produce a new land-life that, in all likelihood, would have no relationship whatever to this postulated pre-Cambrian form.

(And for those of us who are s.f. writers, the way seems open even for pre-Cambrian intelligence. Would they have managed to leave a record somehow? Where? What kind? Would they have launched rockets with frozen "men" aboard to come to life in the far future? Have they come to life? Did they tell Plato the story of Atlantis? Are they manning the flying saucers? —Anyone who wishes may make use of this. No charge.)

Then, when the fury at last died out, the Earth consisted of low-profile continents and shallow oceans. It was, in fact, one vast swampland and conditions must have been ideal for the proliferation of life.

Making up for the hundred million years of death, life-forms diversified and multiplied and then died in the marshes to form fossils. And thus we would have the Great Borning of the Cambrian.

Consider all this, then, and compare it with Velikovsky's dream of an Earth halting its rotation suddenly and accomplishing nothing more than to help Joshua win a battle.

Really!

9. KNOCK PLASTIC!

One of my favorite stories (undoubtedly apocryphal, else why would I remember it?—see the opening paragraphs of Chapter 3) concerns the horseshoe that hung on the wall over the desk of Professor Niels Bohr.

A visitor stared at it with astonishment and finally could not help exclaiming, "Professor Bohr, you are one of the world's great scientists. Surely you cannot believe that object will bring you good luck?"

"Why, no," replied Bohr, smiling, "of course not. I wouldn't believe such nonsense for a moment. It's just that I've been informed it will bring me good luck whether I believe it will or not."

And I too have an amiable weakness—I am an indefatigable knocker of wood. If I make any statement which strikes me as too smug or self-satisfied, or in any way too boastful of good fortune, I look feverishly about for wood to knock.

Of course, I don't for one moment really believe that knocking wood will keep off the jealous demons who lie in wait for the unwary soul who boasts of his good luck without the proper propitiation of the spirits and demons on whom good and bad luck depend. Still—after all—you know—come to think of it—what can you lose?

I have been growing a little uneasy, in consequence, over the way in which natural wood is used less and less in ordinary construction, and is therefore harder and harder to find in an emergency. I might, in fact, have been heading for a severe nervous breakdown, had I not heard a casual remark made by a friend.

He said, some time ago, "Things are going very well for me lately." With that, he knocked on the tabletop and calmly said, "Knock plastic!"

Heavens! Talk about blinding flashes of illumination. Of course! In the modern world, the spirits will grow modern too. The old dryads, who inhabited trees and made sacred groves sacred, giving rise to the modern notion of knocking wood,* must be largely unemployed now that more than half the world's forests have been ground up into toothpicks and newsprint. Undoubtedly they now make their homes in vats of polymerizing plastic and respond eagerly to the cry of "Knock plastic!" I recommend it to one and all.

But knocking wood is only one example of a class of notions, so comforting and so productive of feelings of security, that men will seize upon them on the slightest provocation or on none at all.

Any piece of evidence tending to support such a "Security Belief," however frail and nonsensical it might be, is grabbed and hugged close to the bosom. Every piece of evidence tending to break down a Security Belief, however strong and logical that evidence might be, is pushed away. (Indeed, if the evidence against a Security Belief is strong enough, those presenting the evidence might well be in danger of violence.)

It is very important, therefore, in weighing the merits of any widely held opinion, to consider whether it can be viewed as a Security Belief. If it is, then its popularity means nothing; it must be viewed with considerable suspicion.

* Some people say that knocking wood is symbolic of touching the True Cross, but I don't believe that at all. I'm sure the habit must antedate Christianity.

It might, of course, be that the view is accurate. For instance, it is a comforting thought to Americans that the United States is the richest and most powerful nation in the world. But in all truth, it *is*, and this particular Security Belief (for Americans) is justified.

Nevertheless, the Universe is an insecure place, indeed, and on general principles Security Beliefs are much more likely to be false than true.

For instance, a poll of the heavy smokers of the world would probably show that almost all of them are firmly convinced that the arguments linking smoking with lung cancer are not conclusive. The same heavy majority would exist if members of the tobacco industry were polled. Why not? The opposite belief would leave them too medically insecure, or economically insecure, for comfort.

Then, too, when I was young, we kids had the firm belief that if one dropped a piece of candy into the incredible filth of the city streets, one need only touch the candy to the lips and then wave it up to the sky ("kissing it to God") to make it perfectly pure and sanitary. We believed this despite all strictures on germs, because if we didn't believe it, that piece of candy would go uneaten by ourselves, and someone else, who did believe it, would get to eat it.

Naturally, anyone can make up the necessary evidence in favor of a Security Belief. "My grandfather smoked a pack a day for seventy years and when he died his lungs were the last to go." Or "Jerry kissed candy to God yesterday and today he won the forty-yard dash."

If Grandfather had died of lung cancer at thirty-six, or if Jerry had come down with cholera—no problem, you cite other instances.

But let's not sink to special cases. I have come up with six very broad Security Beliefs that, I think, blanket the field—although the Gentle Reader is welcome to add a seventh, if he can think of one.

Security Belief No. 1: *There exist supernatural forces that can be cajoled or forced into protecting mankind.*

Here is the essence of superstition.

When a primitive hunting society is faced with the fact that game is sometimes plentiful and sometimes not, and when a primitive agricultural society watches drought come one year and floods the next, it seems only natural to assume—in default of anything better—that some more-than-human force is arranging things in this way.

Since nature is capricious, it would seem that the various gods, spirits, demons (whatever you wish to call them) are themselves capricious. In one way or another they must be induced or made to subordinate their wild impulses to the needs of humanity.

Who says this is easy? Obviously, it calls for all the skill of the wisest and most experienced men of the society. So there develops a specialized class of spirit manipulators—a priesthood, to use that term in its broadest sense.

It is fair enough to call spirit manipulation "magic." The word comes from "magi," the name given to the priestly caste of Zoroastrian Persia.

The popularity of this Security Belief is almost total. A certain Influential Personage in science fiction, who is much given to adopting these Security Beliefs, and then pretending he is a member of a persecuted minority, once wrote to me: "Every society but ours has believed in magic. Why should we be so arrogant as to think that everyone but ourselves is wrong?"

My answer at the time was: "Every society but ours has believed the Sun revolved about the Earth. Do you want to settle the matter by majority vote?"

Actually the situation is worse than even the Influential Personage maintains. Every society, *including our own*, believes in magic. Nor do I restrict the belief only to the naïve and uneducated of our culture. The most rational elements of our society, the well educated, the scientists, retain scraps of belief in magic.

When a horseshoe hangs over Bohr's desk (assuming one really did), that is a magical warding-off of misfortune through the power of "cold iron" over a spirit world stuck in the Bronze Age. When I knock on wood (or plastic) I too engage in spirit manipulation.

But can we argue, as the Influential Personage does, that there must be something to magic since so many people believe in it?

No, of course not. It is too tempting to believe. What can be easier than to believe that one can avoid misfortune by so simple a device as knocking on wood? If it's wrong, you lose nothing. If it's right, you gain so much. One would need to be woodenly austere indeed to refuse the odds.

Still, if magic doesn't work, won't people recognize that eventually and abandon it?

But who says magic doesn't work? Of course it works—in the estimation of those who believe.

Suppose you knock on wood and misfortune doesn't follow. *See?* Of course, you might go back in time and *not* knock on wood and find out that misfortune doesn't follow, anyway—but how can you arrange a control like that?

Or suppose you see a pin and pick it up on ten successive days, and on nine of those days nothing much happened one way or the other, but on the tenth, you get good news in the mail. It is the work of a moment to remember that tenth day and forget the other nine—and what better proof do you want anyway?

Or what if you carefully light two on a match and three minutes later fall and break your leg. Surely you can argue that if you had lit that third cigarette, you would have broken your neck, not your leg.

You can't lose! If you want to believe, you can believe!

Indeed, magic can work in actual fact. A tightrope walker, having surreptitiously rubbed the rabbit's foot under his belt, can advance with such self-confidence as to perform perfectly. An actor, stepping out on stage just after someone has whistled in his dressing room, can be so nervous that he will muff his lines. In other words, even if magic doesn't work, belief in magic does.

But then, how do scientists go about disproving the usefulness of magic? They don't! It's an impossibility. Few, if any, believers would accept the disproof anyway.

What scientists do is to work on the *assumption* that Security Belief No. 1 is false. They take into account no capricious forces in their analysis of the Universe. They set up a minimum number of generalizations (miscalled "natural laws") and assume that nothing happens or can be made to happen that is outside those natural laws. Advancing knowledge may make it necessary to modify the generalizations now and then, but always they remain noncapricious.

Ironically enough, scientists themselves become a new priesthood. Some Security Believers see in the scientist the new magus. It is the scientist, now, who can manipulate the Universe, by mysterious rites understood by him only, so as to insure the safety of man under all circumstances. This belief, in my opinion, is as ill-founded as the earlier one.

Again, a Security Belief can be modified to give it a scientific tang. Thus, where once we had angels and spirits descending to Earth to interfere in our affairs and mete out justice, we now have advanced beings in flying saucers doing so (according to some). In fact, part of the popularity of the whole flying saucer mystique is, in my opinion, the ease with which the extraterrestrials can be looked upon as a new scientific version of angels.

Security Belief No. 2: *There is no such thing, really, as death.*

Man, as far as we know, is the only species capable of foreseeing the inevitability of death. An individual man or woman knows, for certain, as no other creature can, that someday he or she must die.

This is an absolutely shattering piece of knowledge and one can't help but wonder how much it, by itself, affects human behavior, making it fundamentally different from the behavior of other animals.

Or perhaps the effect is less than we might expect, since men so universally and so resolutely refuse to think of it. How many individuals live as though they expect to keep on going forever? Almost every one of us, I think.

A comparatively sensible way of denying death is to suppose that it is a family that is the real living entity and that the individual does not truly die while the family lives. This is one of the bases of ancestor worship, since the ancestor lives as long as he has a descendant to worship him.

Under these circumstances, naturally, the lack of children (especially sons, for in most tribal societies women didn't count) was a supreme disaster. It was so in early Israelite society, for instance, as the Bible tells us. Definite rules are given in the Bible that oblige men to take, as wives, the widows of their childless brothers, in order to give those wives sons who might be counted as descendants of the dead man.

The crime of Onan ("onanism") is not what you probably think it is, but was his refusal to perform this service for his dead brother (see Genesis 38:7–10).

A more literal denial of death is also very popular. Almost every society we know of has some notion of an "afterlife." There is someplace where an immortal residue of each human body can go. The shade can live a gray and dismal existence in a place like Hades or Sheol, but he lives.

Under more imaginative conditions, the afterlife, or a portion of it, can become an abode of bliss while another portion can become an abode of torment. Then, the notion of immortality can be linked with the notion of reward and punishment. There is a Security Belief angle to this too, since it increases one's security in the midst of poverty and misery to know you'll live like a god in Heaven, while that rich fellow over there is going straight to Hell, ha, ha, and good for him.

Failing an afterlife in some place beyond Earth, you can

have one on Earth itself by arranging a belief in reincarnation or in transmigration of souls.

While reincarnation is no part of the dominant religious beliefs in the Western world, such are its Security Belief values that any evidence in its favor is delightedly accepted. When, in the 1950s, a rather silly book entitled *The Search for Bridey Murphy* appeared and seemed to indicate the actual existence of reincarnation, it became a best seller at once. There was nothing to it, to be sure.

And, of course, the whole doctrine of spiritualism, the entire battery of mediums and table-rappings and ectoplasm and ghosts and poltergeists and a million other things are all based on the firm insistence of mankind that death does not take place; that something persists; that the conscious personality is somehow immortal.

Is there any use then in trying to debunk spiritualism? It can't be done. No matter how many mediums are shown to be fakes, the ardent believer will believe the next medium he encounters. He may do even better. He may denounce the proof of fakedom as itself a fraud and continue to have faith in the fake, however transparent.

Science proceeds on the assumption that Security Belief No. 2 is false also.

Yet scientists are human too, and individuals among them (as distinct from Science in the abstract) long for security. Sir Oliver J. Lodge, a scientist of considerable reputation, depressed by the death of a son in World War I, tried to reach him through spiritualism and became a devotee of "psychic research."

My friend, the Influential Personage, has often cited Lodge and men like him as evidence of the value of psychic research. "If you believe Lodge's observations on the electron, why don't you believe his observations on spirits?"

The answer is, of course, that Lodge has no security to gain from an electron but does from spirits. —And scientists are human too.

Security Belief No. 3: *There is some purpose to the Universe.*

After all, if you're going to have a whole battery of spirits and demons running the Universe, you can't really have them doing it all for nothing.

The Zoroastrians of Persia worked out a delightfully complicated scheme of the Universe. They imagined the whole of existence to be engaged in a cosmic war. Ahura Mazda, leading countless spirits under the banner of Light and Good, encountered an equally powerful army under Ahriman fighting for Darkness and Evil. The forces was almost evenly matched and individual men could feel that with them lay the balance of power. If they strove to be good they were contributing to the "right side" in the most colossal conflict ever imagined.

Some of these notions crept into Judaism and Christianity, and we have the war of God versus the Devil. In the Judeo-Christian view, however, there is no question as to who will win. God must and will win. It makes things less exciting.

This Security Belief is also assumed to be false by Science. Science does not merely ignore the possibility of a cosmic war, when it tries to work out the origins and ultimate fate of the Universe; it ignores the possibility of any deliberate purpose anywhere.

The most basic generalizations of science (the laws of thermodynamics, for instance, or quantum theory) assume random movement of particles, random collisions, random energy transfers, and so on. From considerations of probability one can assume that with many particles and over long periods of time, certain events are reasonably sure to take place, but concerning individual particles and over short periods of time, nothing can be predicted.

Possibly, no scientific view is so unpopular with nonscientists as this one. It seems to make everything so "meaningless."

But does it? Is it absolutely necessary to have the entire Universe or all of life meaningful. Can we not consider that what is meaningless in one context is meaningful in another; that a book in Chinese which is meaningless to me is meaningful to a Chinaman? And can we not consider that each of us can so arrange his own particular life so as to make it meaningful to himself and to those he influences? And in that case does not all of life and all the Universe come to have meaning *to him?*

Surely it is those who find their own lives essentially meaningless who most strive to impose meaning on the Universe as a way of making up for the personal lack.

Security Belief No. 4: *Individuals have special powers that will enable them to get something for nothing.*

"Wishing will make it so" is a line from a popular song and oh, how many people believe it. It is much easier to wish, hope, and pray, than to take the trouble to *do* something.

I once wrote a book in which a passage contained a description of the dangers of the population explosion and of the necessity for birth control. A reviewer who looked over that passage wrote in the margin, "I'd say this was God's problem, wouldn't you?"

It was like taking candy from a baby to write under that in clear print: "God helps those who help themselves."

But think of the popularity of stories in which characters get three wishes, or the power to turn everything they touch into gold, or are given a spear that will always find the mark, or a gem that will discolor in the presence of danger.

And just imagine if we had amazing powers all the time and didn't know it—telepathy, for instance. How eager we are to have it. (Who hasn't experienced a coincidence and at once cried out "Telepathy!") How ready we are to believe in advanced cases elsewhere since that will improve the possibilities of ourselves possessing the power if we practiced hard enough.

Some wild powers represent the ability to foresee the future—clairvoyance. Or else one gains the knowledge to calculate the future by means of astrology, numerology, palmistry, tea leaves, or a thousand other hoary frauds.

Here we come close to Security Belief No. 1. If we foresee the future, we might change it by appropriate action and this is nearly the equivalent of spirit manipulation.

Is a way, Science has fulfilled the fairy tales. The jet plane goes far faster and farther than the flying horse and the seven-league boots of the fable-writers of yore. We have rockets which seek out their targets, like Thor's Hammer, and do far more damage. We have, not gems, but badges that discolor in the presence of too much accumulated radiation.

But these do not represent "something for nothing." They are not awarded through supernatural agency and don't act capriciously. They are the hard-earned products of the generalizations concerning the Universe built up by a Science that denies most or all of the Security Beliefs.

Security Belief No. 5. *You are better than the next fellow.*

This is a very tempting belief, but it is often a dangerous one. You tell this to that big bruiser facing you and he's liable to break your neck. So you appoint a surrogate: Your father is better than his father; your college is better than his college; your accent is better than his accent; your cultural group is better than his cultural group.

Naturally this fades off into racism and it is not at all surprising that the more lowly the social, economic, or personal position of an individual, the more likely he is to fall prey to the racist temptation.

It is not surprising that even scientists as individuals have trouble with this one. They can rationalize and say that it must surely be possible to divide mankind into categories in such a way that some categories are superior to others in some ways. Some groups are taller than other groups, for instance, as a matter of genetic inheritance. Might it not be that some groups are, by birth and nature, more intelligent or more honest than others?

A certain Nobel Prize winner demanded, some time ago, that scientists stop ducking the issue; that they set about determining whether slum-dwellers (English translation: Negroes) are not actually "inferior" to non-slum-dwellers and whether attempts to help them were not therefore futile.

I was asked by a certain newspaper to write my views about this, but I said I had better tell them, in advance, what my views were going to be, and save myself the trouble of writing an article they wouldn't print.

I said that, in the first place, it was very likely that those who were most enthusiastic for such an investigation were quite confident that they had set up measurement standards by which the slum-dwellers would indeed prove to be "inferior." This would then relieve the superior non-slum-dwellers of responsibility toward the slum-dwellers and of any guilt feelings they might possess.

If I were wrong, I went on to say, then I felt the investigators should be as eager to find a superior minority as an inferior one. For instance, I strongly suspected that by the measurement standards prevailing in our society, it would turn out that Unitarians and Episcopalians would have a higher average IQ and a higher performance record than other religious groups.

If this proved to be so, I suggested, Unitarians and Episcopalians ought to wear some distinctive badge, be ushered to the front of the bus, be given the best seats at the theaters, be allowed to use the cleaner rest rooms and so on.

So the newspaper said, "Forget it!" and it's just as well. No one wants to search out superiors to one's self—only inferiors.

Security Belief No. 6: *If anything goes wrong, it's not one's own fault.*

Virtually everyone has a slight touch of paranoia. With a little practice, this can easily lead one into accepting one of the conspiracy theories of history.

How comforting it is to know that if you're failing in business, it's the unfair crooked tactics of the Bulgarian who owns the store down the block; if you've got a pain, it's because of the conspiracy of Nigerian doctors all about you; if you tripped when you turned to look at a girl, it was some rotten Ceylonese who put that crack in the sidewalk there.

And it is here at last that scientists are touched most closely—

for this Security Belief can turn directly against them for standing out against Security Beliefs in general.

When the Security Believers are stung by the explosion of the hoaxes and follies that deceive them, what is their last, best defense? Why, that there is a conspiracy of scientists against them.

I am myself constantly being accused of participating in such a conspiracy. In today's mail, for instance, I got a most violent and indignant letter, from which I will quote only a couple of mild sentences:

"Not only are we [the public] being played for fools by politicians . . . but now these tactics have spread to science as well. If your purpose is deceiving others for whatever intention, let this tell you that you are not one hundred per cent successful."

I read the letter carefully through and it seemed that he had read some magazine article which had rebutted one of his pet beliefs. He was instantly sure, therefore, not that he himself might be wrong, but that scientists were in a conspiracy against him and were under orders from NASA to lie to him.

The trouble was that he was referring to some article which had been written by someone else, not me—and I didn't know what on Earth he was talking about.

However, I am positive that the forces of Rationality will rise triumphant over the onslaughts of Security Believers despite everything. (Knock plastic!)

PART II

NUMBERS

10. MUSIC TO MY EARS

About ten years ago, in a fit of fatherly pride, I bought a piano and installed it in my living room. My two children (then very young) would, I reasoned, soon reach the age when they could, with very little in the way of actual beating and maiming, be induced to practice. Eventually they would learn to play, and the house would be filled with beautiful music.

Each child, in turn, reached the age of musical apprenticeship, and each practiced for a couple of years with only moderate beating and virtually no maiming. However, my semi-irresistible force had encountered two entirely immovable bodies, and the children won out—bloody, as the saying goes, but unbowed.

So now an unoccupied piano fills the living room and grins at me. I never learned to play the piano myself (or any instrument) but I can't resist beating the keys with one finger now and then and trying to work out the queer hieroglyphics of written music.

Although I usually hit the correct notes, the amount and intensity of objection from the rest of the family whenever I play the piano is indescribable. Nobody thinks that my one-finger rendition of "Dancing Cheek to Cheek" represents true beauty.

Hurt to the core, I have bought myself a small recorder (a little wooden pipe with holes) and I sit with it in my attic and moodily finger it as I blow. I have worked up a rendition of "The First Noel" that peels the wallpaper off the walls, but fortunately, my "Annie Laurie" flattens it right back again.

And now it has occurred to me to exceed all previous feats of intellectual derring-do, and set myself to working out some sense in all these notes I hit and blow, even though I have never studied music in any way.

Here goes, and wish me luck . . .

It all begins with Pythagoras, the Greek philosopher who, about 525 B.C., discovered that two or more strings, plucked together, made a combination of sounds that was pleasing to the ear, if the lengths of those strings were in the ratios of small whole numbers.

Nowadays, we don't talk about lengths of strings, but of frequencies—the number of times per second that the strings beat back and forth in the sound-making vibration. Each musical note has a fixed frequency, and combinations of musical notes sound pleasant when the frequencies are related to each other in ratios of small whole numbers.

For instance, if one frequency is just twice another, the notes blend together perfectly in our ears.

If we take three notes together, then the harmony is particularly good (at least to ears brought up in our particular culture) if the frequencies are in the ratio of 4 to 5 to 6. This combination of notes is called the "major triad."

Well, then, we now have four notes we can rely on to sound good in almost any combination, whether struck consecutively or simultaneously, and these we can label 4, 5, 6, and 8. As you see, 4, 5, 6 make up a major triad and 8 is twice 4.

Next, in order to produce more notes, we ought to see if there is any way we can form a second major triad. Why not consider 8, which is the only one of the four numbers that is not part of a major triad already? Suppose we consider $5\frac{1}{3}$, $6\frac{2}{3}$, and 8. These are in the 4, 5, 6 ratio.

Now we have six numbers: 4, 5, $5\frac{1}{3}$, 6, $6\frac{2}{3}$, 8, making up two interlocking major triads.

But the list of numbers is curiously unbalanced as we have them at this point. The central four notes are clustered together with separations of less than unity. The extreme notes are not so close. The first number, 4, is a full unit removed from its neighbor, 5, while the last note 8 is more than a unit removed from its neighbor, 6⅔. It would be nice if we could fill in those large gaps with members of still a third major triad.

To do that, let's consider that 4 (at one extreme) is the beginning of one triad, and 8 (at the other extreme) the ending of another. Why not build a triad on the number midway between the extremes; 6, in other words? The number 6, 7½, and 9 are in the 4, 5, 6 ratio and 7½ nicely fills the gap between 6⅔ and 8.

Unfortunately that leaves the gap between 4 and 5 still unfilled and supplies us with a 9 that opens a new gap beyond the 8. We can kill two birds with one stone by dividing 9 by 2 and forming another number that will do just as well as 9. (In music, two notes with frequencies in the ratio of 2 to 1 sound very closely related, as I said before.) Half of 9 is 4½, which exactly plugs the hole between 4 and 5.

Now we have the following set of numbers:

4, 4½, 5, 5⅓, 6, 6⅔, 7½, 8

All are separated by intervals of less than unity. Because there are eight notes from 4 to 8 inclusive, the interval from a number to its double is called an "octave." This is from the Latin word for "eight."

These eight numbers represent the common musical scale we use today—the "major scale." There are minor scales and fancy "modes" that were used in ancient and medieval times, but if you think I intend to budge one inch away from the major scale, you are out of your mind.

We can extend the octave in both directions. We can begin with 8 and write another series of numbers each of which is twice the corresponding number of those we already have. Or, beginning at 4, we can work backward to write a series of numbers each of which is half the series of numbers we already have.

We would have, for instance:

first octave—	2,	2¼,	2½,	2⅔,	3,	3⅓,	3¾,	4
second octave—	4,	4½,	5 ,	5⅓,	6,	6⅔,	7½,	8
third octave—	8,	9 ,	10 ,	10⅔,	12,	13⅓,	15 ,	16

Thus, if you go to the piano and strike the white notes in order, you will hear a "tune" that will repeat itself seven times, because the piano covers a little over seven octaves.

What do these numbers mean as far as frequency goes. We can take them literally and say that by 4 we mean a sound wave with a frequency of 4 waves per second. Such a sound wave, however, has a frequency too small to hear.

If we add octaves to the right, however, doubling and redoubling the frequency, we will soon reach audible sounds. Six octaves to the right, we reach one which extends from 256 to 512. These numbers, viewed as frequencies (so many waves per second), make up the middle octave of the piano keyboard —or would, if the 4, 5, 6 ratios were followed exactly. That middle octave would have notes with frequencies:

256, 288, 320, 341⅓, 384, 426⅔, 480, 512

Physicists would be content to work with this because these numbers arise from doubling and redoubling the original 4, 5, 6 ratio. Musicians, however, use as their basic standard the note I have labeled 426⅔, except that they tune it to 440, and then build the entire octave about that. If all the notes of the octave had their frequencies raised in exact proportion (which they don't, as we shall soon see) then the notes of the middle octave of the piano would be:

264, 297, 330, 352, 396, 440, 495, 528

and at least we would get rid of fractions.

Obviously, though, musicians aren't going to call the notes by their frequency numbers. This would be cumbersome even if the musicians of centuries past had known about frequencies. Instead, they used letters and syllables.

One system originated not long after the year 1000. An Italian musicologist named Guido of Arezzo made use of an octave with one note (495) omitted. He also composed (according to tradition) a hymn to John the Baptist, which goes as follows:

Ut queant laxis *re*sonare fibris,
*Mi*ra gestorum *fa*muli tuorum,
*Sol*ve polluti *la*bii reatum,
Sancte Ioannes.

The first italicized syllable was note 264, the second was note 297, and so on up to the sixth italicized syllable which was note 440. From this hymn, which must have been popular, the notes were given the names of the syllables:

264,	297,	330,	352,	396,	440,	—,	528
ut	re	mi	fa	sol	la		ut.

Note 528, you see, begins another octave and is "ut" again, so that we have ut, re, mi, fa, sol, la over and over again.

In the time since Guido, some changes have been made. The gap between 440 and 528 is uncomfortably large and note 495 was very commonly used to fill that gap. It needed a name too, and was given "si." This may very well represent the initials of "Sancte Ioannes" in the final line of Guido's hymn.

There has been a tendency, however, to change the "si" to "ti' in order not to have two notes begin with the same consonant.

Then, too, the monosyllable "ut" is the only one that ends in a plosive consonant, which makes for difficulty in singing the scale with the proper flamboyance. Consequently "ut" was changed to the sonorous "do," with an initial consonant not like any of the others. That gives us:

264,	297,	330,	352,	396,	440,	495,	528
do	re	mi	fa	sol	la	ti	do

which is the scale most of us have been taught to sing.

Another system used is to give the notes successive letters of the alphabet. Since the standard note, the one to which all instruments are tuned, is 440, it is only fair to call it A. The next note, 495, is B, the next, 528, is C, and so on up to G, which is the seventh note. The eighth note is 880, the octave of 440, and it is A again.

Working backward and forward from A, we have the following comparison of the syllable names and the letter names:

do	re	mi	fa	sol	la	ti	do
C	D	E	F	G	A	B	C

The eight notes of the octave (seven really, for the eighth begins a new octave) were worked out entirely from the 4, 5, 6 ratio here in this article. The question, though, is whether the notes are spread more or less equally across the gap of the octave. We can check this by taking the ratio of the frequencies of each successive pair of notes:

$$D/C = 297/264 = 1.125$$
$$E/D = 350/297 = 1.111$$
$$F/E = 352/330 = 1.067$$
$$G/F = 396/352 = 1.125$$
$$A/G = 440/396 = 1.111$$
$$B/A = 495/440 = 1.125$$
$$C/B = 528/495 = 1.067$$

The seven intervals in the octave fall into three groups of ratios. There are three representing a ratio of 1.125, two of 1.111, and two 1.067. The first two, 1.125 and 1.111, are quite close together, while 1.067 is roughly half the size if we consider the figures on the right-hand side of the decimal point, the amount by which the frequency of one note is in excess of the one before. If we lump the first two ratios together as representing "whole intervals" and the third as a "half interval," we can list the scale as follows, including the size of the intervals:

C (1) D (1) E (½) F (1) G (1) A (1) B (½) C

In singing the scale we are used to placing the five whole intervals and the two half intervals exactly as shown above. If we begin with one of the notes representing a C on the piano and hit the white notes successively in either direction, we hear the familiar scale going up or going down and can sing with it. If, however, we start on any note other than C, match our voice to it as "do," and then try to go up or down the scale, we find the piano hits "wrong" notes.

This seriously limits musical flexibility and the thing to do is to fill in the five large intervals with halfway notes, so that one can place a half interval or a whole interval anywhere one wishes all along the piano keyboard. There are five intervals to be filled and the result might be labeled as follows:

```
  X  X     X  X  X
C  D  E  F  G  A  B  C
do re mi fa sol la ti do
```

The five X's are the five halfway notes that fill in the whole intervals in the major scales. They represent the five black notes present in each octave on the piano keyboard. As you see, they have to be arranged in groups of two and three in alternation because that is dictated by the pattern of whole intervals and half intervals.

Counting both white and black notes, there are now thirteen notes in the octave or rather twelve notes, for the thirteenth starts a new octave. These twelve or thirteen are easier to handle than the eight notes were, for the patterns of black keys makes it easy to identify keys. Every white key immediately to the left of the group of two black keys is a C. Every white key immediately to the right of that group is an E and so on.

It is convenient on the piano (though not necessarily on other instruments) to make the twelve intervals in this thirteen-note C-to-C octave exactly equal, in terms of frequency ratios. The second C has a frequency just 2 times that of the first C, so we must have some ratio such that, when twelve of them are multiplied together, the value 2 is reached. That is $x^{12}=2$. It turns out that $x=1.0595$.

If we keep this ratio and build upon the note of A having a frequency of 440, we end up with the eight white keys of the middle octave of the piano having frequencies like this:

261.6 293.7 329.6 349.2 392.0 440.0 493.9 523.2

The five black keys of that same octave would be:

277.1 311.0 370.1 415.5 466.4

How does one name the black notes? In the syllable system, it is possible to have each black note named according to the initial consonant of the note before, followed by an "i," thus:

	di		ri			fi		si		li				
do		re		mi	fa		sol		la		ti	do		

As it happens, the two ordinary notes that are followed by a half interval already end in "i" (mi and ti), which makes for pleasant symmetry.

In the letter system, the black notes are named according to the white notes they adjoin in either direction. If they are related to the white note at the left, they borrow its letter with the added word "sharp" (♯) to indicate the black note is higher than the white (rising up sharply). If they are related to the white note on the right, they borrow its letter with the added word "flat" (♭) to indicate the black note is lower than the white (squatting down flatly).

Thus the black note "ri," between "re" and "mi," is, letter-wise, between D and E. It can be called either D♯ or E♭—that is, "D-sharp" or "E-flat."

In the ordinary scale based on 4, 5, 6 ratios, D-sharp and E-flat need not be exactly identical and the amount by which they vary may differ with where you start the scale. On the piano, however, the black note comes exactly halfway between D and E (in this case), so that D♯ and E♭ are identical.

Each one of the five black notes can be expressed, letter-fashion, only with a sharp or a flat, and each can use either. Thus:

between C and D—C♯ or D♭
between D and E—D♯ or E♭
between F and G—F♯ or G♭
between G and A—G♯ or A♭
between A and B—A♯ or B♭

A sharp raises a note a half interval, and a flat lowers it a half interval. This means that some of the white keys can be expressed by means of sharps and flats. For instance, E and F are half an interval apart and so are B and C. Therefore E could be expressed as F♭ and F could be expressed as E♯. Similarly B could be expressed as C♭ and C could be expressed as B♯. This placing of sharps and flats in the white-key names is not common, but it is legal and, sometimes, useful.

If we list the full range of notes from C to C, counting both black and white notes and, arbitrarily, giving each black note its "sharp" name, we have:

C C♯ D D♯ E F F♯ G G♯ A A♯ B C

There is just half an interval between one of these notes and the next, and to get a whole interval you merely start with any note and move two to the right (or two to the left). Then, too, if you run off the right end (or left end) you just repeat the whole batch of letters and keep on going.

If we want a major scale, we can start anywhere, if we remember to keep the pattern of intervals in the order: whole, whole, half, whole, whole, whole, half.

If we start at C, then it's easy. The white notes are arranged in the proper order and we have:

C D E F G A B C

If we start with D, things are not quite so simple. The first whole interval carries us to E, but the second takes us to F♯. Then the half interval moves us to G. The following whole intervals carry us first to A, then B, but the third takes us to C♯. The final half interval brings us back to D. (The eighth note is always the same as the first.) Thus:

D E F♯ G A B C♯ D

By similar reasoning, we can start with any other note, either white or black, and work out the major scale. Let's use the other white notes in order as starting points, leaving out, for now, note F.

We get:

E	F♯	G♯	A	B	C♯	D♯	E
G	A	B	C	D	E	F♯	G
A	B	C♯	D	E	F♯	G♯	A
B	C♯	D♯	E	F♯	G♯	A♯	B

Each of these scales is identified by its first note. If you begin with C you are in the "key of C" (actually it's "key of C major," but I'm dealing only with major and I don't even want to be reminded there's anything else). Then, in succession, the scales I've given above are the "key of D," the "key of E," the "key of G," the "key of A," and the "key of B."

Notice that in each case the letters progress from the first note to the return of that first note without skipping a single one. Some of them have sharps attached, but that doesn't count as far as the letter is concerned. Indeed, sharps and flats are called "accidentals," as though they are unimportant frills attached to the letter.

Notice also that each of the keys whose scales I have listed above has a different number of sharps.

Suppose we list each key starting with C (or C♯) and ending

with B (why complicate things by repeating C at the end), and suppose also we arrange them in the order of increasing number of sharps. We have:

Key of C—C	D	E	F	G	A	B
Key of G—C	D	E	F♯	G	A	B
Key of D—C♯	D	E	F♯	G	A	B
Key of A—C♯	D	E	F♯	G♯	A	B
Key of E—C♯	D♯	E	F♯	G♯	A	B
Key of B—C♯	D♯	E	F♯	G♯	A♯	B

I don't have to belabor the pleasant pattern that appears here as the sharps gradually build up in number and position. This pattern exhibits itself in musical notation. On the extreme left of each staff, you place no sharps, 1 sharp, 2 sharps, and so on, to indicate where you are making use of the key of C, G, D, and so on. That tells you where you place your "do." The order and position of the sharps placed not only tell you which notes you must routinely sharp if you are to stay in key, but they make a very pretty pattern, too. (In order to show it, I would have to make use of a musical staff and all sorts of symbols, and I beg your indulgence.)

But now let's return to the key of F. If we start with F and try to make a major scale with intervals of whole, whole, half, whole, whole, whole, half, we end up with the following:

F G A A♯ C D E F

We have two A's (the fact that one of them is sharped is irrelevant) and no B. This is not permitted. We must have a B. In order to get one, we must give A♯ its alternate name, B♭. Now we have:

F G A B♭ C D E F

This is the only major scale starting on a white note that must use a flat. (The others can't. If you tried to express them with flats, you would find a letter left out in every case except C, which has neither sharps nor flats.)

Is the key of F the only one with flats? Not at all; there are black keys upon which we can start a scale. If we try those, we find that it is sharps that, in every case, omit a letter. Therefore, we will try all but G♭, using flats only.

As our guide, we will use the complete scale, white and black notes, with the flat names given to the black notes:

C D♭ D E♭ E F G♭ G A♭ A B♭ B C

Using this the key of C still gives us the white keys, C to C inclusive with no flats at all. The key of F gives us the scale included just above, with a single flat. Now let's start with the four black keys, omitting for the nonce G♭.

D♭ E♭ F G♭ A♭ B♭ C D♭
E♭ F G A♭ B♭ C D E♭
A♭ B♭ C D♭ E♭ F G A♭
B♭ C D E♭ F G A B♭

These scales are in the key of D♭, E♭, A♭, and B♭. Let's list the symbols starting with C and ending with B or B♭, in order of increasing numbers of flats, and let's include the keys of C and F. Thus:

Key of C —C D E F G A B
Key of F —C D E F G A B♭
Key of B♭—C D E♭ F G A B♭
Key of E♭—C D E♭ F G A♭ B♭
Key of A♭—C D♭ E♭ F G A♭ B♭
Key of D♭—C D♭ E♭ F G♭ A♭ B♭

Here again is the same pretty pattern—in flats rather than sharps, and the musical notation reflects the prettiness.

But there is still one key left over and that is the key of G♭ which presents special difficulties. If we start with G♭ and follow the thirteen-note octave in its flatted version we get a major scale like this:

G♭ A♭ B♭ B D♭ E♭ F G♭

Of course, we see that the letter C is omitted and that this scale is no good. We can switch from G to the equivalent F♯ and try to use the sharped version of the thirteen-note octave. Now we have:

F♯ G♯ A♯ B C♯ D♯ F F♯

Now the letter E is omitted and apparently we can't write a scale in either the flat or sharp version. This in itself is an interesting symmetry, for we have one key (that of C) which can be written in both the flat and sharp version and here we have one that can be written in neither.

But wait, suppose we write B as C♭ or F as E♯, as I indicated earlier we were permitted to do. In that case, we can write this key in both flats and sharps, thus:

G♭ A♭ B♭ C♭ D♭ E♭ F G♭
F♯ G♯ A♯ B C♯ D♯ E♯ F♯

Now let's put them in the C to B order:

Key of G♭—C♭ D♭ E♭ F G♭ A♭ B♭
Key of F♯—C♯ D♯ E♯ F♯ G♯ A♯ B

As key of G♭, this scale has six flats and fits right at the end of the system of flatted keys, continuing the pattern. And, in its alter ego as the key of F♯, it possesses six sharps and fits the end of the system of sharped keys neatly.

We can therefore set up the following interesting table:

TABLE 10: THE MUSICAL KEYS

Key	*Number of Sharps*	*Key*	*Number of Flats*
C	0	C	0
G	1	F	1
D	2	B♭	2
A	3	E♭	3
E	4	A♭	4
B	5	D♭	5
F♯	6	G♭	6

There are all sorts of symmetries in this table, and you can amuse yourself with them. They don't require pointing out.

All of this, you must understand, is music to my ears and mind, but is nothing at all to my fingers. My mind understands this, but my fingers can't make head or tail out of it. My mind looks at the piano keyboard with infinite satisfaction, and my fingers go "Huh?" All I can do at the piano is tap out something like "Dancing Cheek to Cheek" with one finger.

—But in any key you please.

11. OLD MAN RIVER

Once I had a luncheon date with an editor in order to discuss a possible new book, and we decided to meet at a restaurant at 12:15 P.M. The editor, I might say, was a young lady, for that is not irrelevant to the story.

I must admit, now, that I have a fault that is also not irrelevant to the story. Although nearly perfect in almost every other respect, I do have a tendency to be early to appointments. This means I frequently have to wait, something to which I am completely hardened, and which doesn't bother me. However, when the other party arrives (usually late) there seems to be something about my frank and friendly countenance that indicates I have been waiting a long time and this produces flustered explanations which I dismiss genially.

In this case, I arrived at 12:10 and was shown to a seat. The young lady in question arrived at 12:17 and bore down upon me, explaining as she came.

Naturally, I couldn't allow this. In the first place she was only two minutes late; in the second place, I had only been waiting seven minutes, hardly anything compared to what I am accustomed to; and in the third place, she was a young lady.

So I rose as she reached the table and said in my normal speaking voice (which has a tendency to rattle the distant windows), "Not at all, darling! I've been spending a delightful few minutes here, dreaming of you, and anticipating the ecstasy of your approaching presence!"

—You know, just the usual sort of thing writers are always saying to editors.

A passing waiter stopped in his tracks as I said this, rather as if he had been pole-axed. He turned toward me and stared in growing uncertainty at my sunny blue eyes and my high Slavic cheekbones. Finally he said (with a distinct Italian accent): "Pardon me, sir, but can you possibly be Italian?"

What could I do? Could I hurt his supreme faith in the gallantry of the Italian male? So I said, "Yes, indeed—but only with the ladies."

And he left, thoroughly content.

But it made me think of the manner in which I always try to evade the stereotype. This goes (knock plastic) for my writing as well, which gives no clear indication as to what I "specialize" in.

For instance, I am as interested in geography as in science and when I want to write a geographical essay, I do so.

What sparked the immediate interest was my receipt of a new atlas, *The Odyssey World Atlas*, published by Odyssey Books. It is large, spectacular, and crowded with information, and while I was turning the pages with intense pleasure, I came across a list of rivers. It struck me at once (as it has struck me often before) that the longest river in North America has no name.

The river in question was "discovered" by the Spanish explorer Hernando de Soto in 1541. I put "discovered" in quotation marks because to neglect them would be an exercise in racism. De Soto was the first *European* to see the river, but non-Europeans had discovered it many thousands of years before. It's like the controversy of who *really* discovered America, Christopher Columbus, Leif Ericsson, or St. Brendan—when all along the real discoverer was some nameless Siberian.

The Indians who lived on the riverbanks at the spot reached by De Soto called it "Big River" with admirable straightforwardness. Of course, they called it that in their own language so that it was "Mici Sepe" or something like that. And this became, to Americans and to the world, "Mississippi."

The Mississippi River was taken to be the stream that flowed from Lake Itasca in northern Minnesota, in a generally southward direction, down to the Gulf of Mexico, a length of 2350 miles. In 1783 the western boundary of the United States was established along almost the entire length of this river (the final hundred miles at the mouth remained is the hands of first Spain, and then France, for twenty years more). The name as applied to that particular stretch of flowing water was therefore frozen into American consciousness past all eradication.

Just a few miles north of the city of St. Louis, another river flows into the Mississippi. There is a three-mile stretch of the Mississippi, right in that neighborhood, that runs due north and south with scarcely a wiggle, and the other river comes straight into it from the west at nearly a right angle. This incoming river is called the Missouri River from the name given themselves by an Indian tribe that lived on its banks.

Now, psychologically, one pictures a river as moving straight ahead with a tributary coming in at right angles. Consequently it seemed only natural to think of the Missouri as a tributary of the Mississippi. This was especially so since the Mississippi was a long, long river, known from source to mouth, whereas the Missouri trickled off into the western wilderness somewhere and, for all anyone knew, might conceivably be only a few hundred miles long.

In 1803, however, the United States bought the Louisiana Territory from France (which had no legal right to sell, but it's too late now). Since the Territory included, in theory, the entire drainage area of the western tributaries of the Mississippi, there was importance in determining just where those tributaries went.

In an exploring expedition lasting from 1804 to 1806, Meriwether Lewis and William Clark traced the Missouri River back to its source in what is now southwestern Montana. As it turns out, the Missouri River, following it backward through its longest tributaries, is 2466 miles in length, which makes it a trifle longer than the Mississippi.

But let us now go back to the confluence of the Mississippi and the Missouri just north of St. Louis. When two rivers come together, which is the river and which the tributary? If we want to be logical, we ought to say that the longer of the two joining streams is the river and the shorter is the tributary.

In that case, we have at St. Louis, first, the Missouri, which is 2466 miles long, and, second, the length of the Mississippi above St. Louis (the Upper Mississippi River), which is only 1050 miles long. Clearly it is the Missouri that is the river and the Upper Mississippi that is the tributary.

Imagine a drop of water trickling down the northern slopes of the mountain ridge making up the boundary between the states of Montana and Idaho. It joins something called the Red Rock Creek, which eventually becomes the Missouri River. It is carried through Montana and the Dakotas, along the boundaries between Nebraska and Iowa, into the state of Missouri, joins what we call the Mississippi at St. Louis, flows southward past Memphis, Vicksburg, and New Orleans into the Gulf of Mexico.

From the Montana mountains to the sea, that drop of water has traveled 3760 miles along a single unbroken river, and what is the name of that single unbroken river? It has none! Part of it is called the Missouri and part of it the Mississippi, but the whole of it has no single name. The best we can do is call it the Missouri-Mississippi, which is clumsy and sounds artificial.

The Missouri-Mississippi, though the longest river in North America and the "Old Man River" of the song, is not the longest river in the world. There are two rivers that are longer.

In fact, let's prepare Table 11, containing the "Great Rivers" of the world, using as our criterion for greatness the thoroughly artificial one of a length of a thousand miles or more. Naturally the figures on length are only approximate in some cases, but here goes:

TABLE 11: THE GREAT RIVERS

Great River	*Continent*	*Outflow*	*Length (miles)*
Nile	Africa	Mediterranean Sea	4160
Amazon	S. America	Atlantic Ocean	3900
Missouri-Mississippi	N. America	Gulf of Mexico	3760
Ch'ang (Yangtze)	Asia	East China Sea	3370
Huang	Asia	Yellow Sea	2870
Congo	Africa	Atlantic Ocean	2720
Amur	Asia	Tartar Strait	2700
Lena	Asia	Laptev Sea	2660
Mackenzie-Peace	N. America	Beaufort Sea	2640
Mekong	Asia	South China Sea	2600
Niger	Africa	Gulf of Guinea	2600
Paraná	S. America	Río de la Plata	2580
Ob'	Asia	Gulf of Ob'	2500
Yenisey	Asia	Kara Sea	2410
Murray	Australia	Lake Alexandrina	2310
Volga	Europe	Caspian Sea	2290
Madeira	S. America	Amazon River	2100
Yukon	N. America	Bering Sea	2000
Purus	S. America	Amazon River	1950
St. Lawrence	N. America	Gulf of St. Lawrence	1900
Rio Grande	N. America	Gulf of Mexico	1890
Irtysh	Asia	Ob' River	1840
Syr Dar'ya	Asia	Aral Sea	1810
Brahmaputra	Asia	Bay of Bengal	1800
Indus	Asia	Arabian Sea	1800
São Francisco	S. America	Atlantic Ocean	1800
Danube	Europe	Black Sea	1750
Japurá	S. America	Amazon River	1750
Darling	Australia	Murray River	1725
Euphrates	Asia	Persian Gulf	1710
Tocantins	S. America	Amazon River	1670
Zambeze	Africa	Indian Ocean	1630
Saskatchewan-Nelson	N. America	Hudson Bay	1600
Orinoco	S. America	Atlantic Ocean	1600
Salween	Asia	Gulf of Martaban	1600
Ural	Asia-Europe	Caspian Sea	1570

Great River	*Continent*	*Outflow*	*Length (miles)*
Amu Dar'ya	Asia	Aral Sea	1550
Ganges	Asia	Bay of Bengal	1550
Paraguay	S. America	Paraná River	1530
Arkansas	N. America	Missouri-Mississippi	1450
Colorado	N. America	Gulf of California	1450
Dnieper	Europe	Black Sea	1420
Negro	S. America	Amazon River	1400
Si-Kiang	Asia	South China Sea	1380
Angara	Asia	Yenisey River	1300
Allegheny-Ohio	N. America	Missouri-Mississippi	1300
Irrawaddy	Asia	Andaman Sea	1300
Orange	Africa	Atlantic Ocean	1300
Pilcomayo	S. America	Paraguay River	1300
Columbia	N. America	Pacific Ocean	1210
Don	Europe	Sea of Azov	1210
Sungari	Asia	Amur River	1170
Tigris	Asia	Persian Gulf	1160
Upper Mississippi	N. America	Missouri-Mississippi	1050
Snake	N. America	Columbia River	1040
Red	N. America	Missouri-Mississippi	1020
Churchill	N. America	Hudson Bay	1000
Uruguay	S. America	Río de la Plata	1000

There are thus 58 Great Rivers on the Earth, which may be divided up among the continents as in Table 12:

TABLE 12: GREAT RIVERS BY CONTINENTS

Asia	21
North America	14
South America	12
Africa	5
Europe	5
Australia	2

The total here comes to 59 because the Ural River forms the entirely artificial boundary between Europe and Asia and is counted to both.

We might say that among the Great Rivers are four "Super Rivers" with lengths of more than 3000 miles, distributed, neatly enough, one to a continent. Africa boasts the Nile, South America the Amazon, North America the Missouri-Mississippi, and Asia the Ch'ang (better known to me, at least, as the Yangtze).

And yet this is an illusion. Judging by every criterion *but* length, there is only one Super River. Suppose, for instance, that we consider the area of land drained by a river and its tributaries. The Ch'ang (Yangtze) drains something less than a million square miles, while the Nile and the Missouri-Mississippi drain something more than a million. None of the three are in first place. None of them are even in second place.

Judging by the size of the drainage area, the Congo River, which is only in sixth place in length, and is distinctly below the 3000-mile mark, does much better than the stretched-out Nile. It has a drainage area of 1,600,000 square miles.

And at that, the Congo is only in second place. Surpassing it easily is the Amazon, which, with its tributaries, drains about 2,700,000 square miles. The discrepancy becomes even greater if we compare drainage areas to the total continental area. After all, a South American river has less potential area to drain than an Asian river has, simply because South America is the smaller continent. If we do this, the results, in Table 13, look as follows:

TABLE 13: DRAINAGE BASINS

River	*Continent*	*Fraction of Continent Drained*
Ch'ang (Yangtze)	Asia	0.05
Nile	Africa	0.09
Missouri-Mississippi	North America	0.13
Congo	Africa	0.14
Amazon	South America	0.40

In this respect, the Amazon is incomparable.

We can conclude precisely the same thing if we consider the volume of water delivered by the rivers. The Nile, despite its great length, flows through the desert for a thousand miles and loses much water by evaporation. It delivers a comparatively small volume to the sea, therefore. The Missouri-Mississippi and its tributaries discharge 675,000 cubic feet of water per second into the ocean. The Ch'ang (Yangtze) does rather better with a mark of 770,000 and the Congo does still better with 1,200,000 cubic feet per second. However, the Congo is only second best. I cannot find the precise figures for the Amazon River in my library, alas, but I remember reading once that its volume of discharge was seven times that of the second most voluminous river, which would make it some 8,000,000 cubic feet per second.

Let's see if we can't do something for the Amazon River in terms of length as well.

The Great Rivers, if we look at the table, fall into two classes. There are, first, main rivers that flow into oceans, gulfs, bays, or inland seas. Then there are tributaries that flow into larger rivers. Among the Great Rivers are seventeen tributaries that are themselves Great Rivers. Let's pull them out of the list and look at them in Table 14:

TABLE 14: GREAT TRIBUTARIES

Tributary	*River*
Madeira	Amazon
Purus	Amazon
Irtysh	Ob'
Japurá	Amazon
Darling	Murray
Tocantins	Amazon
Ganges	Brahmaputra
Paraguay	Paraná
Arkansas	Missouri-Mississippi
Negro	Amazon
Angara	Yenisey
Allegheny-Ohio	Missouri-Mississippi
Pilcomayo	Paraguay
Sungari	Amur
Upper Mississippi	Missouri-Mississippi
Snake	Columbia
Red	Missouri-Mississippi

As you see, the Amazon has five tributaries that are themselves Great Rivers. In fact, of the six longest tributaries in the world, no less than four are tributaries of the Amazon. This includes the longest tributary of all, the Madeira River—the only river in the world that manages to be longer than 2000 miles and then ends up merely in another river.

No other Great River can match this. The Missouri-Mississippi has four Great River tributaries, but they are from the short half of the list whereas the Amazon's are from the long half. The Paraná has two such tributaries, but those two form a unique combination. It has a Great River tributary and a Great River *sub*-tributary. The Pilcomayo flows into the Paraguay which, in turn, flows into the Paraná, and all three are Great Rivers. There is no other case like that on Earth. Six other Great Rivers; Ob', Murray, Brahmaputra, Yenisey, Amur, and Columbia, have one Great River tributary apiece.

Suppose now that we add up lengths. Let us add to the length of each Great River the length of each Great River tributary and call the total length that of the "Great River System." It turns out there are eight such Great River Systems over 3000 miles in length, and there are also two Great Rivers which have no Great River tributaries but which are themselves over 3000 miles long. Let's add them in and list the ten of them in Table 15:

TABLE 15: GREAT RIVER SYSTEMS

Great River Systems	*Total Length (miles)*
Amazon	12,770
Missouri-Mississippi	8,580
Paraná	5,310
Ob'	4,340
Nile	4,160
Murray	4,035
Amur	3,870
Yenisey	3,710
Ch'ang (Yangtze)	3,370
Brahmaputra	3,350

Of these ten Systems, five are in Asia, two are in South America, and one each is in North America, Africa, and Australia. The three largest, oddly enough, are in the Western Hemisphere.

But as you can see the Amazon Great River System is far longer than any other, so that length joins volume of flow and drainage area to mark out the uniqueness of that river.

The Amazon River is *the* Old Man River; no other stream need apply. There is sober truth in saying that all the rivers in the world fall into two classes. The first includes the Amazon River. The second includes all the rest.

Now, for another point. Consider the fate of the Great Rivers, their point of outflow.

In the table of the Great Rivers, I gave the outflow as seas, gulfs, bays, and so on. Actually, we can be more fundamental. Each river that reaches the open sea, either directly, or by way of the larger river into which it flows, ends up in one of the three great divisions of the ocean. These are the Pacific Ocean, the Atlantic Ocean (including the Arctic Ocean), and the Indian Ocean.

If we look at it that way then the five longest Great River Systems all flow into the Atlantic Ocean. (The longest that does not is the Murray-Darling in Australia and that, while long, is a mere trickle of a river that doesn't amount to much.)

Suppose, then, we become systematic and go back over our list of Great Rivers, counting how many of them flow into each ocean, and finding the total mileage in each case as in Table 16.

TABLE 16: GREAT RIVERS BY OCEANS

Ocean	*Great Rivers*	*Total Length (miles)*
Atlantic	34	66,060
Pacific	10	19,790
Indian	10	16,585

There is no question but that the Atlantic Ocean receives most of the river water in the world. Not only does it receive more Great Rivers with a longer total mileage than the other two oceans combined but among the rivers flowing into the Atlantic are the very largest—the Amazon and the Congo.

Notice, by the way, that there are 54 Great Rivers that drain off into the three oceans, whereas there are 58 Great Rivers altogether. There is no mystery here; the discrepancy has a simple explanation. There are four Great Rivers that never reach the ocean. Here they are in Table 17:

TABLE 17: GREAT RIVERS WITHOUT OCEANS

Great River	*Outflow*
Volga	Caspian Sea
Syr Dar'ya	Aral Sea
Ural	Caspian Sea
Amu Dar'ya	Aral Sea

The Caspian Sea and the Aral Sea are both inland and each receives two Great Rivers; the only inland bodies of water to do so. The Volga River thus has the distinction of being not only the longest river in Europe but also the longest river anywhere in the world that never reaches the ocean.

As it happens three and a half of these four rivers are to be found entirely within the territory of the Soviet Union. The headwaters of the Amu Dar'ya form part of the border between the Soviet Union and Afghanistan.

Interestingly enough, these Great Rivers are rather poor in large cities. Such cities tend to cluster on the shores of lakes or oceans. When they are on rivers, the rivers are very often small. London is on the Thames River (209 miles long), Paris on the Seine (480 miles), Berlin on the Spree (220 miles), and Moscow on the Moskva (315 miles).

Consider the American Great River System, the Missouri-

Mississippi. Not one of America's million-and-over cities is to be found upon it. We have five cities with a population of over a million, and of these, one is on the Atlantic Ocean, one on the Pacific Ocean, one on Lake Michigan, and one on Lake St. Clair. The fifth is on a river but not a Great River.

The largest city on all the thousands of miles of the Missouri-Mississippi System is St. Louis and its population is only 750,000.

Can you guess, then, which is the largest city in the world to be on a Great River in an inland location? (Close your eyes and try.) Now look at the answer and see if you're right.*

* Answer: Cairo, Egypt. It is on the Nile and has a population of 3,518,000.

12. CROWDED!

What with one thing or another, I give a number of talks here and there, and these talks are usually followed by a question-and-answer period. That is the fun part—or the agony part, depending on how things go.

Very often the game of place-the-speaker-on-the-spot is played and the speaker, if he happens to be in rare form, can win with a quick and unexpected bit of repartee. The reward is a roar of laughter from the audience that is more warming than the honorarium.

I wish I could say that I am always ready with the crushing retort, but, alas, I am not.

Sometimes I come through, however, and an example that shall live forever in my memory came once, just after I had looked at my wristwatch and said, as is customary, "I'm afraid we have time for only one more question."

Whereupon a young man in the audience jumped to his feet and said, "Dr. Asimov, could you give us, in the time remaining, your impression of what the world of the future will be like?"

And, without any perceptible hesitation, I answered, "Crowded!" and walked off the platform to a thunder of laughter and applause. (Oh, boy, if I could only do that every time.)

But you know, it isn't the world of the future alone that is going to be crowded. We are already crowded and I would like to demonstrate that fact in a way that has not yet been done to death.

For instance, I live in a suburb of Boston, and no one can call Boston a small town. It is not a huge metropolis, but it is a thoroughly respectable city. It has a population of just about 616,000 and it is the largest city in New England.

And how many cities in the world do you think are larger than Boston? You may guess before you read further, if you wish.

Well, checking through the latest data in my library, I would estimate that there are at least 150 cities in the world that are larger than Boston. And somehow, as I stand in the shadow of the Prudential Tower and look about at the not-more-than 151st largest city in the world, I feel a little shrunken.

To be sure, Boston's boundaries are only an imaginary line on the map. Her houses and population spill over that line in every direction into a ring of suburbs; and the metropolitan area, or Greater Boston as it is called, has a population of some 2,600,000.

But we can't use that for comparison. Other cities have their metropolitan areas too. Besides, a "metropolitan area" is not a single political entity. Each one of Boston's suburbs (and there are several dozen) has its own mayor, police and fire department, school system, and tax practices. This means that the "metropolitan area" is a hazy thing indeed, which grows and shrinks according to which suburbs you decide belong to it and which you decide don't. No, no, if we are going to try to come to some conclusions concerning cities, we had better choose something that is hard and fast and that is the political city line.

There are a dozen cities in the United States alone that are larger than Boston, and, of these, six have a population of more than a million, within the city limits proper. One million is a nice round number, so let's define a Great City, quite arbitrarily, as one that has a population of a million or more. The six Great Cities of the United States are, in order of population,* given in Table 18:

* I am not using the 1960 Census figures but the latest estimates I can find. I am doing the same for foreign cities where the estimates are often quite rough and unreliable, but what can you do?

TABLE 18: GREAT CITIES OF THE UNITED STATES

City	*Population*
New York	8,080,000
Chicago	3,520,000
Los Angeles	2,740,000
Philadelphia	2,030,000
Detroit	1,600,000
Houston	1,100,000

The total population of these six Great Cities is just about 19,000,000, and counting the population of the United States as about 195,000,000, this means that 9.7 percent of the American population, or just about 1 American in every 10, lives in a Great City. Consider the near-Great Cities and add the suburbs to all of them and our vision of small-town America vanishes in a puff of cliche.

But before you get so saddened you can't continue, let's ask a few questions, possibly amusing ones, concerning American cities. You'll find the answer at the back of the article but see how you do, first, without consulting maps and atlases. (I must admit I did.)

1. What is the largest city in the United States that is only the second largest city in its state?

2. What American city comes closest to being a Great City without being one?

3. The various American states tend to pick small cities as capitals out of a traditional distrust for big city "mobs." What is the largest city to serve as capital of a state?

4. What is the smallest?

Now let's move on. There are three countries that are more populous than the United States and they are China (750,000,000), India (475,000,000) and the Soviet Union (230,000,000). Each, naturally, is rich in Great Cities. Let us begin with China, which (see Table 19) has no less than sixteen Great Cities according to the best figures I can get:

TABLE 19: GREAT CITIES OF CHINA

City	*Population*
Shanghai	7,000,000
Peking	6,800,000
Mukden	3,100,000
Tientsin	2,900,000
Harbin	2,500,000
Chungking	2,200,000
Canton	2,150,000
Sian	1,500,000
Paotow	1,500,000
Taiyuan	1,500,000
Nanking	1,400,000
Lanchou	1,200,000
Poshan	1,200,000
Hsinking	1,150,000
Tsingtao	1,120,000
Chengtu	1,100,000

This seems an amazing collection of huge cities at first glance, but it is less amazing if you stop to think about it.

Consider first how many Great Cities there are in the world altogether. (Care to make a quick guess before I tell you?) Well, there are eighty-nine altogether. China has nearly one-fifth of all of them within her borders, but why not? She has more than one-fifth the population of the world within her borders, after all.

The total population of these sixteen Great Cities of China is about 38,000,000, just twice the Great City population of the United States. But then, China has three and a half times our population. Only 5 percent of China's population, or 1 out of 20, lives in a Great City. Compare this with our own 1 out of 10.

India has six Great Cities (Table 20) and the Soviet Union has seven (Table 21):

TABLE 20: GREAT CITIES OF INDIA

City	*Population*
Bombay	4,540,000
Calcutta	3,005,000
Delhi	2,300,000
Madras	1,840,000
Ahmedabad	1,250,000
Hyderabad	1,150,000

TABLE 21: GREAT CITIES OF THE SOVIET UNION

City	*Population*
Moscow	6,334,000
Leningrad	3,218,000
Kiev	1,292,000
Gorky	1,066,000
Tashkent	1,061,000
Kharkov	1,048,000
Novosibirsk	1,013,000

The total population in the Great Cities of these countries is almost the same. It is 15,000,000 for the Soviet Union and 14,000,000 for India. However, India's total population is far greater than that of the Soviet Union and that is reflected in the concentration of population within them. Whereas 6.5 percent of the population of the Soviet Union live in its Great Cities, only 3 percent of the population of India do.

But we are not through. There are many nations less populous than the United States and one of them, with just half our population, nevertheless has seven Great Cities, one more than we do. You may have guessed that the nation is Japan. Its seven Great Cities are given in Table 22:

TABLE 22: GREAT CITIES OF JAPAN

City	*Population*
Tokyo	8,730,000
Osaka	3,200,000
Nagoya	1,900,000
Yokohama	1,600,000
Kyoto	1,285,000
Kobe	1,115,000
Kitakyushu	1,000,000

The total Great City population in Japan is 18,800,000, nearly that of the United States. One out of every five Japanese lives in a Great City.

All other nations have fewer Great Cities within their individual borders than do any of those already mentioned, but put them all together and there are forty-seven Great Cities remaining. These are listed in Table 23 in order of population:

TABLE 23: THE REMAINING GREAT CITIES

City	*Nation*	*Population*
London	Great Britain	8,185,000
Cairo	Egypt	3,518,000
Rio de Janeiro	Brazil	3,223,000
Mexico City	Mexico	3,193,000
São Paulo	Brazil	3,164,000
Seoul	South Korea	2,983,000
Buenos Aires	Argentina	2,967,000
Djakarta	Indonesia	2,907,000
Paris	France	2,780,000
Rome	Italy	2,455,000
Madrid	Spain	2,443,000
Teheran	Iran	2,317,000

City	*Nation*	*Population*
Sydney	Australia	2,256,000
West Berlin	West Germany	2,193,000
Melbourne	Australia	2,003,000
Karachi	Pakistan	1,913,000
Budapest	Hungary	1,900,000
Hamburg	West Germany	1,856,000
Milan	Italy	1,666,000
Vienna	Austria	1,634,000
Barcelona	Spain	1,634,000
Bangkok	Thailand	1,608,000
Caracas	Venezuela	1,590,000
Alexandria	Egypt	1,588,000
Bogotá	Colombia	1,488,000
Istanbul	Turkey	1,467,000
Lima	Peru	1,436,000
Saigon	South Vietnam	1,336,000
Lahore	Pakistan	1,296,000
Pusan	South Korea	1,271,000
Bucharest	Romania	1,236,000
Warsaw	Poland	1,232,000
Naples	Italy	1,221,000
Montevideo	Uruguay	1,203,000
Montreal	Canada	1,191,000
Munich	West Germany	1,182,000
Manila	Philippines	1,139,000
Turin	Italy	1,117,000
Birmingham	Great Britain	1,106,000
Johannesburg	South Africa	1,095,000
East Berlin	East Germany	1,071,000
Guadalajara	Mexico	1,048,000
Glasgow	Great Britain	1,036,000
Taipei	Nationalist China	1,028,000
Prague	Czechoslovakia	1,011,000
Surabaya	Indonesia	1,008,000
Kinshasa (Leopoldville)	Congo	1,000,000

We can now summarize this information, first by nations, then by continents and finally for the entire planet.*

There are thirty-seven nations in the world that contain at least one Great City, and I will list them in Table 24 in order of total Great City population to the nearest hundred thousand:

TABLE 24: GREAT CITIES BY NATIONS

Nation	*Number of Great Cities*	*Total Great City Population*
China	16	38,000,000
United States	6	19,000,000
Japan	7	18,000,000
Soviet Union	7	15,000,000
India	6	14,000,000
Great Britain	3	10,300,000
Italy	4	6,500,000
Brazil	2	6,400,000
West Germany	3	5,200,000
Egypt	2	5,100,000
South Korea	2	4,300,000
Australia	2	4,300,000
Mexico	2	4,200,000
Spain	2	4,100,000
Indonesia	2	3,900,000
Pakistan	2	3,200,000
Argentina	1	3,000,000
France	1	2,800,000
Iran	1	2,300,000
Hungary	1	1,900,000
Austria	1	1,600,000
Thailand	1	1,600,000
Venezuela	1	1,600,000
Turkey	1	1,500,000
Colombia	1	1,500,000
Peru	1	1,400,000

* I suppose that I ought to apologize for all these statistics but consider—if all else fails, what topics of conversation these will make available for cocktail parties. "Guess how many cities there are with populations of more than a million?" you can begin.

Nation	Number of Great Cities	Total Great City Population
South Vietnam	1	1,400,000
Canada	1	1,200,000
Poland	1	1,200,000
Romania	1	1,200,000
Uruguay	1	1,200,000
Philippines	1	1,100,000
East Germany	1	1,100,000
South Africa	1	1,100,000
Czechoslovakia	1	1,000,000
Nationalist China	1	1,000,000
Congo	1	1,000,000

Of course, total numbers aren't everything. What about Great City concentration of population? As I said earlier, 9.7 percent of the population of the United States lives in Great Cities, but this is considerably exceeded by the percentage of the Japanese population that lives in Great Cities.

Does Japan hold the record? It does not. Three nations (see Table 25) exceed its concentration of Great City population:

TABLE 25: GREAT CITY CONCENTRATION

Nation	Percent of Population in Great Cities
Uruguay	45
Australia	38
Austria	22

Uruguay offers an astonishing spectacle. Almost half the population of that small land (a trifle larger than North Dakota in area) is squeezed into Montevideo, its capital and one Great City. The only thing I can think of which is comparable is the situation in New York State, somewhat smaller in size than Uruguay, but six and a half times as populous. Here 45 percent of New York State's population squeezes into its one Great City, New York City.

Australia is almost as lopsided. Almost two-fifths of its entire population dwell in its two Great Cities of Sydney and Melbourne. (It suddenly occurs to me that there are no less than 12 English-speaking Great Cities. This is surpassed only by the 16 Chinese-speaking ones.)

Perhaps even more astonishing is the case of Austria. Nearly one-quarter of its population crowds into its single Great City of Vienna. This must be considered in its historic setting. Prior to World War I, Vienna was capital of Austria-Hungary, a much larger country than present-day Austria. The capital suited the country, but after World War I, Austria-Hungary was hacked into fragments and Vienna remained as the giant capital of a small remnant of the nation.

Budapest remained as the giant capital of another small remnant, so that nearly one-fifth of Hungary's population is crowded into that Great City.

There is a tendency among the older nations to have a Great City as their capital. Indeed, Warsaw, Paris, London, Bucharest, and many others grew and became Great Cities just because they were capitals.

Some of the newer nations, however, less encrusted with tradition, have deliberately created a capital, or adopted one, which is not a Great City, even though Great Cities are present and available in the nation. This is especially true of the English-speaking countries, with the glaring exception of Great Britain itself. Thus, we have Washington, D.C., United States; Canberra, Australia; and Ottawa, Canada; all of which are not Great Cities. In nations long under English-speaking domination, we have Quezon City, Philippines; New Delhi, India; and Rawalpindi, Pakistan; again not Great Cities. Which leads me to:

5. There are three other nations among those possessing Great Cities which have non-Great City capitals. Which are they and what are the capitals?

Great Cities tend to exist in groups. The closest pair are West Berlin and East Berlin which are contiguous, but that is the accident of Cold War politics. They are essentially a single city, split between two governments.

Leaving that abnormal case to one side, the closest pair of Great Cities is Tokyo and Yokohama in Japan. The city limits of these two approach within four miles of each other. Compare this with the ninety miles that separate New York and Philadelphia, the closest American pair of Great Cities. Indeed, Japan also contains the best example of a Great City triplet. A squat triangle only thirty-five miles on its longest side will contain Kyoto, Osaka, and Kobe. So:

6. What is the most northerly of the Great Cities? The most southerly?

7. What is the most populous nation *not* to contain a Great City.

But let's pass on to continents. Suppose we count offshore islands with the nearest continent: Japan and Indonesia with Asia, Great Britain with Europe, and so on. Let's remember, too, that although Turkey is largely an Asian country, Istanbul is in the small segment of it that is in Europe. Let us remember, further, that two of the Great Cities of the Soviet Union (Tashkent and Novosibirsk) are in Asia. We have, therefore, in Table 26:

TABLE 26: GREAT CITIES BY CONTINENTS

Continent	*Number of Great Cities*	*Total Great City Population*
Asia	42	91,700,000
Europe	25	51,300,000
North America	9	24,200,000
South America	7	15,100,000
Africa	3	6,100,000
Australia	2	4,300,000

The population of Europe and North America is more concentrated than that of Asia and South America. About 8 percent of the population of the first two continents live in the Great Cities, as compared with not more than 5 percent of the population of the last two. Africa is far behind, with a concentration of only about 2 percent. It is Australia that carries off the award, though. Even counting New Zealand as part of the continent, the concentration is still 25 percent.

The total population of the eighty-eight Great Cities of the world is just about 193,000,000, almost exactly the population of the United States. This includes one out of every seventeen human beings on the Earth today.

And the number of Great Cities will increase each year, together with the total population living in them, both in actual numbers and in percentages of all humanity. I estimate that in the last half decade alone, the list of Great Cities has increased by seven and their total population by 13,000,000.*

Where it will all end, I don't know. I can only wait in terror as each day is more crowded than the one before.

Answers

1. Dallas Texas, population 790,000—outstripped by Houston, Texas.

2. Baltimore, Maryland, with a population of 925,000.

3. Boston, Massachusetts, (aha!) but the distinction may not be lasting. Boston's population is dropping quickly (80,000 in the last six years) and capital cities such as Denver, Colorado, may overtake it before long.

4. Juneau, Alaska; population 7200.

5. Bonn, West Germany; Brasilia, Brazil; and Ankara, Turkey.

6. Leningrad is farthest north, Melbourne farthest south.

7. You would naturally look for this nation in the most under-concentrated continent, Africa. It turns out to be Nigeria, which has a population of 56,400,000 and is the ninth most populous nation on Earth. It doesn't have a single Great City. Its largest city, Lagos (its capital), has a population of 665,000.

* Naturally, it is impossible to keep an essay like this up to date. I have received letters since its first publication stating that Guadalajara, Mexico, has moved into the Great City class; informing me that Seoul's population is now 3,800,000, and so on. What can I do . . .

13. RIGHT BENEATH YOUR FEET

I am inordinately fond of the name Isaac. Partly this is because it happens to belong to me, but mostly it is because it is rather uncommon as first names go. This means I am not plagued, ordinarily, by other Isaacs. When someone says Isaac they generally mean me, and I answer if I am within earshot.

Of course, there was Isaac Newton, but, as anyone knows who follows my essays, I am a great admirer of his, and, besides, he is long since dead. I am more than a little discomfited, however, at the current popularity of Isaac Bashevis Singer, who is not only a living Isaac, but who is also a writer.

Yet such Isaacs at least reflect credit on the name. What about those who, for one reason or another, do not?

It was in this connection that I received a recent shock. Having been busily engaged in sopping up information from an encyclopedia, in connection with some little job or other, my eye happened to fall upon the entry CANTON (Illinois). There, under the subheading "History," it said in letters of clearest print:

> The town was founded in 1825 by Isaac Swan. . . . The founder . . . named his town Canton in the belief that Canton, China, was directly opposite on the globe.

How embarrassing for an Isaac to think this. It is possible to see at once, without looking at a map or globe, that Canton,

China, is not on the side of the globe directly opposite to Canton, Illinois. In fact, we can go further and say that no point in China is on the side of the globe directly opposite any point in the United States. Let us go further still and say that no point anywhere in Europe or Asia is directly opposite any point in North America.

But by now you have guessed that Isaac Swan's mistake hasn't embarrassed me to the point where I am unable to write an essay on the subject. And in fact I intend to do so, and right now, too!

The Greeks were the first to have worked out the fact that the Earth was spherical in shape, and they were the first, therefore, to worry about what the other side of the planet might be like.

Perhaps there was some feeling among the Greeks just at first that they themselves lived on top of the Earth (their eyes told them that much) and that any person attempting to live on the other side would fall off. Youngsters today, on first learning that the Earth is shaped like a ball, probably have that same initial worry.

By Aristotle's time, however, it was plain that "up" and "down" were relative terms; that all matter on Earth tended to the center, and that "down" was therefore in the direction of one's feet wherever one stood upon the planet. The other side of the Earth could therefore well be inhabited.

Nevertheless, even if men did not fall off the other side of the Earth, there was no question but that relative to one's self, those on the other side were upside down. If you could see right through the Earth, you would observe the feet of men on the other side pointing "upward" toward you.

Whether you considered those feet as being located on the opposite side of the globe, or as pointing in the direction opposite to that in which yours were pointing, the term to use for them would, in either case, be "antipodes." This is from Greek words meaning "opposite feet."

Many of the ancient and medieval geographers, knowing that

it grew generally hotter as one traveled south, surmised that the equatorial belt on Earth was uninhabitable and unpassable because of its blazing heat. If this were so, the Earth would be divided into two halves that would be forced to remain forever out of touch.

The temperate regions north of the equator were known to be inhabited, of course. The temperate regions south of the equator might be inhabited too, but before 1400 European geographers could not tell. They could only try to work it out by deduction from first principles or, if they preferred, from the inspired words of the Bible. The unknown and unknowable half of the Earth was sometimes referred to, broadly, as the antipodes and it can be used, even today, to refer to the southern hemisphere.

Such a broad meaning of the term, however, has been rendered useless by the fifteenth-century discovery, on the part of Europeans, that the equator could, after all, be crossed. Let us therefore restrict the word to its narrow meaning.

In the narrow sense, one ought to speak of an antipodal point; that is, that point which is directly opposite to the point on which you are standing. If you were to dig a hole straight down, you would (if you could) reach the center of the Earth and, continuing, eventually come into the open again at the antipodal point, having dug through nearly 8000 miles of rock and molten metal.

Or suppose we confine ourselves to the surface of the Earth and pretend that surface is absolutely smooth, ideally spherical, and exactly 25,000 miles in circumference. (All of these pretenses are actually quite reasonable approximations of the truth.) In that case, if we traveled 12,500 miles in *any* direction, we would end up at the same point—the antipodal point.

Next step: What can we tell about the antipodal point without looking at a map?

Let's begin by considering latitude. Suppose you are standing at a point which is at a latitude of x°N. In order to reach the antipodal point you would have to drop an imaginary line through the center of the Earth.

When that line reaches the center, it is at a latitude of 0°* for the center of the earth is in the equatorial plane. (To see this, imagine yourself to be slicing the Earth across the various parallels of latitude. If so, only the slice along the equator, at a latitude of 0°, would cut through the center. If your imagination fails you, look at a globe.)

Well, then, if the latitude of the imaginary line has dropped from x°N to 0° in passing from your position to the center of the Earth, and thus completing half its journey, it should, in the remaining half of its journey, by a simple consideration of the symmetry of the situation, pass from 0° to x°S.

We conclude, then, that for any point at a latitude of x°N, the antipodal point must be at a latitude of x°S. Contrariwise, for any point at a latitude of x°S, the antipodal point is at a latitude of x°N.

This gives us enough information for several interesting conclusions.

1. For any point at 90°N, the antipodal point is at 90°S and vice versa. But there is only one point on Earth that is at 90°N and only one at 90°S, the north pole and south pole respectively. The north pole and south pole are therefore antipodal to each other.

2. For any point at a latitude of 0°, the antipodal point must also be at a latitude of 0°. Therefore, for any point on the equator, the antipodal point is also on the equator.

3. For any point in the northern hemisphere, the antipodal point must be in the southern hemisphere, and vice versa. Therefore, if two points are both in the northern hemisphere (or both in the southern hemisphere) they cannot be antipodal to each other and you can reach that conclusion without consulting any map or globe. Since all of Europe, Asia and North America are

* The 0° latitude marks the line of the equator. This divides the northern hemisphere from the southern, and is not itself either north or south latitude, and should therefore be marked neither N or S, but simply 0°.

in the northern hemisphere; no point in any portion of these continents can be antipodal to any other point. In particular Canton, China, cannot be antipodal to Canton, Illinois, and so much for Isaac Swan.

Let's consider longtitude, next. By arguments similar to those for latitude, we can conclude that any point in the eastern hemisphere must have an antipodal point in the western hemisphere and vice versa. If two points are both in the eastern hemisphere or both in the western hemisphere, one cannot possibly be antipodal to the other.

But let's go further. Each meridian is a "great circle," passing through both north and south poles. (A great circle is a circle, drawn on the surface of a sphere, and lying on a plane, passing through the center of the sphere and cutting the sphere in two equal parts. Thus, a plane slicing through any meridian will pass through the center of the earth and will cut the Earth into two equal halves.)

If you start at some point on a particular meridian, and draw an imaginary line straight downward, it will pass through the center of the Earth and then out to the surface of the Earth on another point on the same meridian. This is true for *any* great circle, and not just for meridians. It is true for the equator, for instance, as I pointed out earlier, the equator being the only parallel of latitude that is a great circle.

The catch about meridians of longitude, however, is that they do not bear the same label all the way around the Earth. Each of them is divided into two halves with different labels. Thus if the 0° meridian is followed past the north or south pole, it becomes the 180° meridian.* If the 10°E meridian is followed past the north or south poles it becomes the 170°W meridian. If the 50°W meridian is followed past the north or south pole it becomes the 130°E meridian.

In general, a meridian marked y°E becomes (180—y)°W, and

* The 0°/180° meridian divides the Earth into an eastern and western half. The meridian is not itself either East Longitude or West Longitude, and is written simply 0° or 180° without an appended E or W.

one marked y°W becomes (180—y)°E, when these are followed beyond the poles. If a point is located on any particular meridian, its antipodal point is located on the other half of that particular meridian.

We can summarize then by saying that if a point on the Earth's surface has a location of x°N, y°W, its antipodal point has a location of x°S, (180—y)°E. This system holds for any combination of N or S and E or W, provided we remember to replace N by S (and vice versa) and W by E (and vice versa) in passing from point to antipodal point.

Now let's go back to Canton, Illinois, the town founded by Isaac Swan. It is located at just about 40.6°N, 90°W. Its antipodal point must therefore be 40.6°S, 90°E. (The 90° meridian is the only one that doesn't change its number on passing the poles, since 180—90=90, but it does change from W to E and vice versa.)

The point antipodal to Canton, Illinois, lies in the Indian Ocean, about 1600 miles southwest of Perth, Australia, the nearest bit of continental land. And it is about 4600 miles from Canton, China.

In fact, suppose we work out a patch of the Earth's surface that is antipodal to the forty-eight contiguous states of the United States. The United States stretches, roughly speaking from 50°N to 30°N and from 70°W to 125°W.

The antipodal patch, then, would be from 50°S to 30°S and from 110°E to 55°E, *and that entire area is ocean.* In other words, if you dig straight down from any point in the forty-eight states, you are almost certain to emerge in the watery wastes of the southern Indian Ocean.

In this whole watery stretch, the largest piece of dry land is Kerguelen Island, named for the French navigator Kerguelen-Tremarec, who discovered it in 1772. It is an unattractive island (its alternate name is Desolation Island), owned by France, and located about 1400 miles north of the coast of Antarctica. It has an area of 1300 square miles, making it about one-third larger than the state of Rhode Island. Its location is 49°S, 70°E, so that its antipodal point is 49°N, 110°W.

This means that there is a Rhode Island-sized patch of land, where the boundary of Montana meets with the junction of the Canadian provinces of Alberta and Saskatchewan, which has the dignity of being the only region in North America where one can dig straight down and come through upon a sizable piece of dry real estate. The American town nearest the place is Kremlin, Montana, and the nearest Canadian town is Jaydot, Alberta.

The only other patches of land I can find in the antipodal section of the Indian Ocean are two small islands, Amsterdam Island and St. Paul Island, both also French possessions. Amsterdam is 25 square miles in area, a trifle larger than Manhattan Island, while St. Paul is only 3 square miles in area. The former is at 38°S, 77°E, while the latter is 38.7°S, 77.5°E. The antipodal points to those islands are, respectively, 38°N, 103°W, and 38.7°N, 102.5°W.

The points antipodal to those two islands are both in east-central Colorado. If anyone happens to be about 7 miles southeast of Las Animas, Colorado, and digs straight down, he will emerge on Amsterdam Island. If he is about the same distance southeast of Karval, Colorado, he will emerge on St. Paul Island.

These are distinctions, I suspect the two towns are unaware of.

What about Alaska and Hawaii, however?

The antipodal patch for the bulk of Alaska lies roughly between a latitude of 60°S and 70°S and a longitude of 12°E and 40°E. This patch is to be found in the ocean south of Africa and covers no land of consequence. It skims the coastline of Antarctica without significant contact.

For that matter, the antipodal patch for Canada lies between those for Alaska and the United States and is also in the south Indian Ocean. The archipelago north of Canada has as its antipodal regions, various portions of the continent of Antarctica. For instance, the antipodes of Victoria Island off north-central

Canada lies along the Ingrid Christensen Coast and the Merv Ice Shelf in Antarctica.

Other arctic land areas also have sections of the coast of Antarctica as antipodes. The antipodes of northern Greenland lies in Victoria Land and along the coast of the Ross Ice Shelf. The Tamyr Peninsula in north-central Siberia, has, as its antipodes, portions of the Palmer Peninsula (a name recently changed to the Antarctic Peninsula). The northernmost tip of the Palmer Peninsula, the only portion of the Antarctic continent to jut considerably beyond the Antarctic Circle, has its antipodal point deep in Siberia, about 300 miles west of the city of Yakutsk.

But the bulk of the Antarctic continent has, as its antipodal patch, the Arctic Ocean. This would be even truer if the Antarctic ice sheet were not counted as dry land. Most of that section of Antarctica which serves as the antipodes for parts of Siberia probably has no true dry land under the ice.

And Hawaii, our fiftieth state? That is different. Its antipodal patch is in southern Africa. Thus, Honolulu, which is located 21.3°N, 157.8°W, has, as its antipodal point, 21.3°S, 22.2″E, and that point is just a bit north of the town of Ghanzi in Botswana.

Note this. The forty-nine continental states of the United States are opposite ocean. The fiftieth state, an island-region deep in the ocean, is opposite a continent.

We are bound to ask the question, then: Which continental regions have, as their antipodes, other continental regions? We have already noted that North America is opposite the Indian Ocean and that Antarctica is opposite the Arctic Ocean. What about the other continents?

Let's see: The antipodal patch of Africa is entirely in the southwest Pacific, and the antipodal patch of Europe is also there but farther south. The antipodal patch of Australia is entirely in the North Atlantic.

That leaves South America and Asia. The antipodal patch of

giant Asia stretches across the width of the South Pacific and laps over into southern South America. To put it more specifically, the nations of Argentina, Chile, and Uruguay have as their antipodal patch a large section of eastern China, while northwestern South America is directly opposite southeast Asia.

Cape Horn, the southern tip of South America, stretches so far south, that its antipodal point reaches (symmetrically) so far north as to fall into south central Siberia near a town called Tsipikan.

Is all this coincidence? Why is it that continents are almost invariably opposite oceans on our globe?

For one thing, the continental land areas make up only 30 percent of the surface of the globe; which means that it is much more likely that a section of ocean, rather than a section of continent, be antipodal to any point on a continent. Then, too, we must consider the peculiar distribution of land on the Earth.

Imagine, to begin with, a planet divided into two hemispheres, one of which is entirely land and the other entirely water. In that case, every bit of land would have as its antipodal point a stretch of water, even though the land surface made up 50 percent of the planet.

Oddly enough, this is almost the case with the earth. If you manipulate a globe of the earth so that you center the Pacific Ocean in your direction, you will find you are staring at a hemisphere that is almost entirely water. The only continental land areas visible would be Australia, Antarctica, and the rims of Asia and North America. With the Earth's land surface squeezed almost entirely into a single hemisphere, it is no wonder that continental areas so rarely lie opposite continental areas.

But, then, why is the Earth's land surface squeezed almost entirely into a single hemisphere? One possibility is that they are correct who visualize a primitive Earth in which the entire land surface made up a single gigantic continent—"Pangaea." Pangaea broke up and the fragments drifted apart but even after some billions of years the drifting has not carried matters to the point where the dry land has gotten much beyond the single hemisphere within which it originated.

Apparently, South America has drifted far enough to allow a portion of itself to be directly opposite a portion of Asia. The continents of Australia and Antarctica ought to have found continental opposition for themselves, too, but through a strange coincidence (or is it a coincidence?) both have found themselves antipodal to stretches of the new ocean that formed, gradually, between the major fragments of Pangaea as they drifted apart.

Yet if that is the case: Why did Earth's land surface originate as a single continent? What caused this odd asymmetry in Earth's development? Frankly, I don't know, so we might just as well leave the problem at this point.

I would like to include in this article Table 27, which is of a sort you cannot find (to my knowledge) anywhere else. It includes some of the important cities of the Earth, their latitude and longitude, and the latitude and longitude of their antipodal point. I don't include all the cities by any means, and my humble apologies are hereby tendered to the inhabitants of any of the omitted cities.

TABLE 27: ANTIPODAL POINTS

	Location		*Antipodal Point*	
City	*Lat.*	*Long.*	*Lat.*	*Long.*
Leningrad, U.S.S.R.	59.9 N	30.3 E	59.9 S	149.7 W
Moscow, U.S.S.R.	55.7 N	37.5 E	55.7 S	142.5 W
Berlin, Germany	52.5 N	13.4 E	52.5 S	166.6 W
London, England	51.5 N	0	51.5 S	180
Paris, France	48.8 N	2.3 E	48.8 S	177.7 W
Budapest, Hungary	47.5 N	19.3 E	47.5 S	160.7 W
Rome, Italy	41.9 N	12.5 E	41.9 S	167.5 W
Chicago, U.S.A.	41.8 N	87.6 W	41.8 S	92.4 E
Istanbul, Turkey	41.0 N	29.0 E	41.0 S	151.0 W
New York, U.S.A.	40.5 N	73.5 W	40.5 S	106.5 E
Madrid, Spain	40.4 N	3.7 W	40.4 S	176.3 E
Philadelphia, U.S.A.	40.0 N	75.1 W	40.0 S	104.9 E
Peking, China	38.8 N	116.5 E	38.8 S	63.5 W

City	Location Lat.	Location Long.	Antipodal Point Lat.	Antipodal Point Long.
Seoul, Korea	37.7 N	127.0 E	37.7 S	53.0 W
Teheran, Iran	35.7 N	51.4 E	35.7 S	128.6 W
Tokyo, Japan	35.5 N	139.8 E	35.5 S	40.2 W
Los Angeles, U.S.A.	34.0 N	118.2 W	34.0 S	61.8 E
Shanghai, China	31.3 N	121.5 E	31.3 S	58.5 W
Cairo, U.A.R.	30.5 N	31.3 E	30.5 S	148.7 W
Canton, China	23.1 N	113.3 E	23.1 S	66.7 W
Calcutta, India	22.5 N	88.3 E	22.5 S	91.7 W
Mexico City, Mexico	19.5 N	99.1 W	19.5 S	80.9 E
Bombay, India	18.9 N	72.8 E	18.9 S	107.2 W
Saigon, South Vietnam	10.8 N	106.7 E	10.8 S	73.3 W
Singapore, Singapore	1.3 N	103.8 E	1.3 S	76.2 W
Djakarta, Indonesia	6.1 S	106.9 E	6.1 N	73.1 W
Sydney, Australia	33.9 S	151.2 E	33.9 N	28.8 W
Buenos Aires, Argentina	34.6 S	58.3 W	34.6 N	121.7 E

With the table completed, here are a few interesting tidbits about antipodal points.

The antipodes of London falls on the 180° meridian well south of the equator; about 600 miles southeast of New Zealand as a matter of fact. The nearest land of any sort to London's antipodal point consists of a group of rocky islands with a total area about that of Manhattan. They belong to New Zealand and are located some 150 miles northwest of London's antipodal point. And what is the name of this group of islands. Aw, come on. Guess!

Give up? Okay, they're the Antipodes Islands.

As for Shanghai, China, its antipodal point falls on the boundary of Uruguay and Argentina, just about 225 miles due north of Buenos Aires. I'm sure that this is the most remarkable pair of nearly antipodal cities, since Shanghai has a population of about 7,000,000 and Buenos Aires one of about 3,000,000. This is the only case of antipodal Great Cities (see Chapter 12). The antipodal point of Peking, China, is only about 80 miles west of Bahia Blanca, Argentina. This is an even closer example of sizable antipodal cities, but Bahia Blanca is no Great City. Its population is about 120,000.

We ought to mention the antipodal point of Canton, China, too, since it is that which started this article. It is not at Canton, Illinois, of course, or anywhere in North America. Instead, it is on the South American continent, almost exactly at the point where the boundaries of Argentina, Chile, and Bolivia meet.

The antipodal point of Sydney, Australia, is in the North Atlantic about 250 miles south of the Azores Islands.

The antipodal point of Djakarta, Indonesia, is in the Colombian Andes, about 125 miles north of Bogotá. That of Singapore is in eastern Ecuador, among the headwaters of the Amazon River.

Finally, the antipodal point of Saigon, South Vietnam, is in central Peru, also in the headwaters of the Amazon. I mention this last item only so that those who have had enough of Saigon and all it represents will know exactly where to go to get as far away as possible.

And let me know when you're leaving. I may join you.

14. THE TIMES OF OUR LIVES

A number of years ago, I had occasion to call a friend of mine, who lives far far away. I am here in Massachusetts and he is in California and I know there is three hours difference in the time.

Noting it was 9 A.M. by my watch, I decided to call him at once and catch him at precisely noon before he had a chance to go out to lunch. I reached him without trouble. I was my usual ebullient self, but there seemed to be a certain constraint about him which bothered me a bit.

Finally I said, "Is there anything wrong, old boy?"

And he (the politest man in the world) said, "Not really. I'm just not at my best at 6 A.M."

Alas, alas, in my haste I had added three hours to the time on my watch instead of subtracting them.

But that's not the end of the story.

Not long afterward, I wrote a book on time measurement and I thought it would be funny to include the story on the back flap where the little biographical squib goes. The publisher thought so too, except that he didn't think it would reflect well for the author of a book like that to own up to such a mistake, so, without consulting me, he reversed matters, and said that someone had called *me* at the wrong time.

How's that for adding insult to injury? Fortunately they didn't mention my friend's name and I hereby make amends. It was all *my* stupidity.

And despite that thorough advertisement of my incompetence, I shall discuss time zones anyway.

The fundamental time of day is noon because that can be measured unequivocally. Noon is when the center of the Sun coincides with the line of the meridian. (The meridian is the imaginary north-south line passing through the observer's zenith.)

As nearly as we can judge by the way things feel, the interval from one noon to the next stays just about the same from noon to noon to noon to noon.

If we manufacture a clock that will turn its hands at an absolutely constant and appropriate speed, we will find that our feelings are just about right. If the clock is adjusted so that it registers 12 when the Sun crosses the meridian, it will register 12 again when the Sun next crosses the meridian, and 12 again when the Sun next crosses the meridian and so on.

Or, at least, it will *almost* register 12 each noon. If we adjust the clock so that it will mark exactly 24 hours to the day, we will find that in the course of the year, the time at which the Sun crosses the meridian will rarely be exactly noon. And adjusting the clock to make it go a little slower or faster will never correct matters. No matter how the clock is regulated, it will never mark off the noons properly, as long as it ticks at a constant rate.

But if the clock's hands turn at a constant rate, and if the Earth rotates at a constant rate, what's the problem? Astronomy is the problem. If the Earth's orbit were an exact circle and if its axis had zero inclination, then noon would come on the dot of 12 each day of the year as measured by a constant clock. But the Earth's orbit is an ellipse, and the Earth's axis is tipped a little more than twenty-three degrees to the plane of the ecliptic and these factors introduce an irregularity.

Thus, if the Sun crossed the meridian at exactly 12:00:00 on December 20, it would cross it just a trifle after 12:00:00 the next day, and a trifle later still the next day, and so on. By early February, the Sun would be crossing the meridian at 12:16 P.M. Then it would start crossing earlier and earlier. It would be back at 12:00 April 15, be down to 11:54 A.M. on May 15, back to 12:00 on June 20, to 12:06 P.M. on August 1; back to 12:00 on September 1; out to 11:44 A.M. on November 5, and back to 12:00 on December 20.

Obviously you can't have a Sun and a clock that keep slipping past each other back and forth from day to day in a monotonous and complicated dance, even if it does all average out in the course of the year.

We have to choose between three alternatives: 1) We follow the Sun and ignore the clock; 2) we follow the clock and ignore the Sun; 3) we adjust the clock to a variable speed that just matches the antics of the Sun, and follow both.

But consider how convenient it is to tell time to the minute by a clock and how difficult to do the same by the Sun. Consider also how difficult it is to work out the gears that would match a clock to the Sun. It is no wonder, then, that as soon as accurate clocks were invented in the mid-seventeenth century, the second alternative was taken and the Sun was immediately dismissed.

In place of the real Sun which crosses the meridian in an irregular fashion, astronomers have invented a "mean Sun" which crosses the meridian regularly and on the dot, every 12:00:00 (as marked by an ideally accurate clock) on every day of the year.

Time that is based on the actual passing of the real Sun across the meridian is called "apparent time." Time based on the crossing of the mean Sun is "mean time." And need I say that "mean" is roughly synonymous to "average"?

The relationship between mean time and apparent time in the course of the year is expressed by the "Equation of Time." The easiest way of representing the Equation of Time graphically is by means of a lopsided figure-eight which you will find somewhere in the Pacific Ocean on most sizable globes. It is called an "analemma" and if you study it carefully, you will be able to work out the difference between apparent time and mean time for every day of the year.

Mean time differs with one's longitude. Every one who is standing on precisely the same north-south line on the Earth's surface has the same meridian overhead, and the mean Sun crosses it for all of them together. If one person stands to the east of another, his meridian (the more easterly) is crossed first by the mean Sun, which is coming from the east. The mean Sun, in its apparent motion from east to west (as the Earth rotates under it from west to east) crosses, in succession, all the mathematically infinite number of meridians on the surface of the globe in twenty-four hours.

The east-west circle drawn around the Earth at the Equator, or along any line parallel to the equator ("parallels of latitude") is marked off in 360 degrees of arc (360°). If it takes 24 hours for the Sun to traverse all 360°, it takes it $\frac{24}{360}$ hours, or 4 minutes, to traverse 1°.

Since there are 60 minutes of arc (60′) to each degree and 60 seconds of arc (60″) to each minute, it takes the Sun $\frac{4}{60}$ minutes, or 4 seconds, to traverse 1′; and $\frac{4}{60}$ seconds or 0.067 second to traverse 1″.*

Let's see what this means, practically. The city of Boston is at a latitude of about 42°20′N. At that latitude, one degree of arc along an east-west line is equal to 51.3 miles. One minute of arc is equal to 1505 yards and one second of arc to 25 yards.

My house is just about 9.2 miles due west of the State House in Boston, or about 10.8 minutes of arc. Imagine the mean Sun just crossing the meridian at the State House. It will take it 43.2 seconds to cross the 10.8 minutes of arc between the State House and my house. Therefore, when it is 12:00:00 at the

* It would be so neat if seconds and minutes were made only 1/15 as long as they are. It would then take the Sun 1 "short-second" to traverse 1″ and 1 "short-minute" to traverse 1′. Sixty such "short-minutes" would then make up a "degree of time" in which the Sun would traverse 1°. Fifteen degrees of time would make an hour and twenty-four hours would make a day. However, no one in the world would want to go through the madness of the transition to such a new time scale, just so that the Earth's meridians would become a perfect match for Earth's clocks and thrill my sense of neatness.

State House, it is only 11:59:16.8 A.M. at my house. And when the mean Sun reaches the meridian of my house so that I am at 12:00:00, then it is 12:00:43.2 P.M. at the State House. These are examples of what I might call "individual mean time."

Indeed, we can go farther. My house is not a mathematical point. Its widest east-west extension is about 20 yards or 0.8 seconds of arc. That means there is a twentieth of a second of difference in time between the place in which I sleep and the place in which I type. My typewriter is west of my bed, so when it is 12:00:00.00 at my typewriter it is 12:00:00.05 P.M. at my bed.

It is, of course, ridiculous to bother with "individual mean time." If there were a great huge "town clock" on top of the dome of the State House which I could see from my window, I would cheerfully set my watch by it and be hanged with the 43 seconds one way or the other. Being a little off from the mean Sun would be as nothing compared to the convenience of having a clock that agreed exactly with all the other clocks in the Metropolitan Boston area.

In fact, as late as the mid-nineteenth century, it was customary to take one's time from the town clock or its equivalent. In place of individual mean time, there was "local mean time," the mean time that was held constant over an entire locality. And if a town twenty-five miles west decided to run its own local mean time 2 minutes earlier than the local mean time of your own town, well, that was all right, too.

In 1850, then, that portion of Earth's surface which had accurate clocks as part of its culture was divided up into an incredible patchwork of local mean times.

But by 1850, railroads were beginning to weave their steel networks across various nations and for the first time, sizable quantities of people undertook to make routine overland trips. For rail travel to be efficient and reliable, trains had to arrive and leave "on time." If they did not do so, passengers would be forced to wait for unconscionable lengths of time at the station or, far worse, arrive just as a train was vanishing off into the distance.

The railroad was the first everyday phenomenon in the history of mankind which made "the exact minute" a meaningful rather than a metaphoric phrase. Until then, there was nothing (except perhaps for astronomical observations) that required of the average man any precision in time closer than "when the Sun is just past zenith" or "in the second watch of the night when the Wain verges on yon distant steeple."

So the trains started putting out timetables to guide prospective passengers and found at once they could not use local mean time. Local mean time varied from point to point along the railroad and any attempt to use Podunk time for Podunk and Squeedunk time for Squeedunk ground down into miseries for all concerned. It was simply necessary to establish a local mean time that would cover an entire railroad network.

To do that, you would eventually have to establish that local mean time as applying not only to railroads but to everything else. People just won't use one time for themselves and another time for the railroad and walk around with a table of conversions to use whenever they want to catch a train.

Fortunately for themselves, those nations which most quickly built up a rail network in the mid- and late-nineteenth century, had a relatively small east-west extension, and there were but small time differences involved.

In Great Britain, for instance, the time difference between London and Glasgow is 16 minutes. In France, the time difference between Strasbourg and Best is 45 minutes. In Germany (using nineteenth-century boundaries), the time difference between Aachen and Konigsberg was just about 1 hour.

In such nations, a single local mean time could be established for the entire rail network and the entire nation, and nobody would be differing from the Sun by more than a few minutes. The discrepancy was a microscopic price to pay for the enormous convenience gained.

(Just the same, I'll bet that when the order came to the town of Niederschlagen or Pompomterre or Swanslea-on-the-Wicket to alter the town clock by seven minutes to adjust to the national standard, there were loud outcries by some against "tampering with God's time.")

In exactly two nations in the nineteenth century was the solution a difficult one, for there were two nations that combined a rapidly growing rail network with an enormous east-west extension. Those nations were, of course, Canada and the United States. The time difference between Portland, Maine and Portland, Oregon, is about 3.5 hours, while that between Halifax and Vancouver is about 4 hours.

No single time could be conveniently established for all of the United States and Canada, and for a while each railroad system used its own time standards. The result was chaos with a capital K.

Through hindsight, the solution is childishly simple. It was simply to divide a large east-west nation into strips, within each of which there would be a set "standard time," and with a one-hour difference from one strip to its neighbor.

This idea was first advanced and fought for by Sandford Fleming of Canada and Charles F. Dowd of the United States. I mention them chiefly because like so many benefactors of mankind they have been rewarded by total obscurity.

Now let's see how such time-strips work. We can begin with the 0° meridian—the "Prime Meridian" or the "Greenwich Meridian" (because it passes through the Greenwich Observatory in London)—and suppose that it is precisely noon there.

It takes the mean Sun just one hour to traverse 15 degrees from east to west. It will therefore be one hour before it reaches 15°W, and when it is noon at 0°, it is 11 A.M. at 15°W. By the same reasoning it is 10 A.M. at 30°W, 9 A.M. at 45°W, and so on.

Going back to the Prime Meridian, we can see that it took the mean Sun just one hour to reach it from a point 15 degrees to the east. By the time it is noon at 0°, it is therefore 1 P.M. at 15°E and, by similar reasoning, 2 P.M. at 30°E, and so on.

We can indeed set up Table 28, matching longitude and time. Furthermore, we can simplify the time-markings by doing away with the ridiculous A.M. and P.M. bit. We can simply count the hours from 1 A.M. to noon as 1 to 12 and then continue onward with 1 P.M. as 13, 2 P.M. as 14 and so on till we reach midnight as 24. This system is used in the armed forces, but I approve of it anyway and wish it would come into general and world-wide use.

Imagine, next, that we divide the surface of the Earth, with mathematical exactness into twenty-four strips like the segments of a tangerine, each strip centering about one of the meridians in Table 28. Each strip would represent a "standard time zone" and would stretch from 7.5° east of the central meridian to 7.5° west of it. Thus, the time zone from 7.5°W to 7.5°E would be the one centering on the Prime Meridian.

Four such standard time zones cross the forty-eight contiguous states of the United States. In theory, they are:

1) 127.5°W to 112.5°W, centering about 120°W.
2) 112.5°W to 97.5°W, centering about 105°W.
3) 97.5°W to 82.5°W, centering about 90°W.
4) 82.5°W to 67.5°W, centering about 75°W.

These are given names that are applicable to the geographic situation within the United States: 1) Pacific standard time zone; 2) Mountain standard time zone; 3) Central standard time zone; 4) Eastern standard time zone. It is hopeless ever to try to give up these names, but it must be realized that they are purely local. The same time zone that embraces eastern United States (and is therefore called "Eastern") covers western South America. The "Mountain" zone, which covers the Rocky Mountain area, in other places stretches over trackless ocean.

So let's speak of time zones on a planetary scale by some device that is not local. The labels ought to have planet-wide significance.

We could label each zone by its centrally placed meridian,

TABLE 28: THE TIME ZONES

Meridian	*Time (12-hour)*	*Time (24-hour)*
180°	midnight	24
165° W	1 A.M.	1
150° W	2 A.M.	2
135° W	3 A.M.	3
120° W	4 A.M.	4
105° W	5 A.M.	5
90° W	6 A.M.	6
75° W	7 A.M.	7
60° W	8 A.M.	8
45° W	9 A.M.	9
30° W	10 A.M.	10
15° W	11 A.M.	11
0°	noon	12
15° E	1 P.M.	13
30° E	2 P.M.	14
45° E	3 P.M.	15
60° E	4 P.M.	16
75° E	5 P.M.	17
90° E	6 P.M.	18
105° E	7 P.M.	19
120° E	8 P.M.	20
135° E	9 P.M.	21
150° E	10 P.M.	22
165° E	11 P.M.	23
180°	midnight	24

and speak of 75°W standard time instead of "Eastern standard time." Or, to simplify it further, we could call it "Zone 75 West." This is not bad, but it is not dramatic enough. Since the whole purpose of these time zones is to standardize the marking of time, why not call each zone by its time.

If we start with the time zone centering about the Prime Meridian at the conventional time of noon, you can call that time zone "Zone 12" (using the armed forces method of marking the hours of the day).

If you check Table 28, you will see that if the Prime Meridian is at 12, then 75°W is at 7. Since 75°W centers the Eastern standard time zone, we can call it "Zone 7." Similarly, Central standard time is in "Zone 6," Mountain standard time in "Zone 5," and Pacific standard time in "Zone 4."

In theory now, everyone who knows his own longitude, or can find it on a map, ought to know in which time zone he is—but that's counting without the political and economic facts of life.

The boundary between Zone 7 and Zone 6 is the 82.5°W meridian. That goes right through the middle of the states of Ohio and Georgia.

It is inconvenient for a state to have part of itself in one Time zone and part in another. To have Cleveland in Zone 7 while Cincinnati is in Zone 6; or Savannah in Zone 7 while Atlanta is in Zone 6; would be inconvenient and would introduce unnecessary complications in the state government and economy.

Well, what one decides to have a clock face say is entirely a matter of arbitrary decision. Ohio and Georgia both decided to have their clocks agree with the great centers to the east and the entire state is, in each case, in Zone 7.

Similarly, the western section of Texas (more than half of the state) is in Zone 5, but the large cities in eastern Texas: Dallas, Fort Worth, Houston, and Galveston are in Zone 6. Texas has decided to place itself in Zone 6. (El Paso in extreme west Texas puts itself, unofficially, into Zone 5, however.)

This sort of irregularity, introduced to make the Time zones suit man-made boundaries and the economic facts of life is found everywhere in the world. Thus, eastern Brazil, with its large cities of Rio de Janeiro and São Paulo is in Zone 9. Uruguay and most of Argentina are, in theory, in Zone 8. However, such are the practical benefits of having a unified time over the entire area, that both Uruguay and Argentina have declared themselves entirely within Zone 9. Even western Argentina, which is actually within Zone 7 (*my* zone) is legally in Zone 9.

In the same way, Great Britain is entirely within Zone 12, while Scandinavia and central Europe are within Zone 13. France and Spain are, properly speaking, in the same Zone as Great Britain, but the land connection with central Europe and the convenience of a rail network without a time jump is such that France and Spain place themselves in Zone 13.

Very few nations in the world allow themselves to have more than one Zone. They subject themselves to the inconvenience of time differences within their own boundaries only when the east-west extension is so great as to make it absolutely unavoidable.

The record number of time zones within a single political unit are the eleven making up the Soviet Union. Its western boundary is in Zone 14, its eastern boundary in Zone 24. When it is 2 P.M. in Moscow, it is midnight at the Bering Strait.

There are four Zones in the 48-stretch of the United States but three more if Alaska and Hawaii are included, for seven altogether. In Table 29, I list the various nations with more

TABLE 29: NATIONS WITH SEVERAL TIME ZONES

Nation	*Number of Time Zones*
Soviet Union	11
United States	7
Canada	7
Mexico	3
Brazil	3
Indonesia	3
Australia	3
Pakistan	2
Congo	2
China	2

than one time zone, with the warning that I am not sure about China. According to my maps, Manchuria is in Zone 21, while all the rest of China is declared in Zone 20, even though the land stretches westward across Zones 19, 18, and 17. I suspect that most of the Chinese west follows its own local standards and that the official time means little.

There are other complications, too. There are some places which prefer not to choose between the coarse division of one hour or the next. If they are near the boundary between two zones they may prefer to place themselves on the half-hour mark. Thus, Iran, which is partly in Zone 15 and partly in Zone 16, declares all of itself to be in Zone 15.5. In other words, when it is noon in London, it is 3:30 P.M. in Iran. Similarly Afghanistan is in Zone 16.5, India in Zone 17.5, and Burma in Zone 18.5.

There are even odder decisions. Guyana, the new nation on the northern coast of South America, is in Zone 8.25. A few patches of the Earth are without any legal time zones at all. These include places like the Mongolian People's Republic, Saudi Arabia, Greenland, and Antarctica.

Daylight Saving introduces other complications with which I won't get involved here. In addition, there is the matter of the International Date Line, which I will take up in the next chapter.

From what I've said then, you can see that the time zones, so simple and regular in concept, are forced by the practical state of things to writhe like wounded snakes (and to shift from time to time, too). I wish I could describe each time zone but words are inadequate. Instead, I will, for your amusement, list in Table 30 the largest city in each time zone.

Then, in order to get *all* the details, I recommend that you study a good, large-scale, multicolor map. If you're anything like me, by the time you come up for air, you will find that your own local time has somehow advanced several hours and a load of work remains to be done.

But there might be a gain, too. For instance, I have it perfectly clear now that I am in Zone 7 and my California friend is in Zone 4 and when it is 9 A.M. on my clock it is 6 A.M. on his.

TABLE 30: THE LARGEST CITIES OF THE TIME ZONES

Zone	*Largest City*
1	Nome, Alaska
2	Honolulu, Hawaii
3	White Horse, Canada
4	Los Angeles, California
5	Denver, Colorado
6	Chicago, Illinois
7	New York, New York
8	Santiago, Chile
8.5	St. John's, Newfoundland
9	Rio de Janeiro, Brazil
10	Ponta Delgada, Azores
11	Reykjavik, Iceland
12	London, England
13	Paris, France
14	Moscow, Soviet Union
15	Istanbul, Turkey
15.5	Teheran, Iran
16	Sverdlovsk, Soviet Union
16.5	Kabul, Afghanistan
17	Karachi, Pakistan
17.5	Bombay, India
18	Novosibirsk, Soviet Union
18.5	Rangoon, Burma
19	Djakarta, Indonesia
19.5	Singapore, Singapore
20	Peking, China
21	Tokyo, Japan
21.5	Adelaide, Australia
22	Sydney, Australia
23	Petropavlovsk, Soviet Union
24	Christchurch, New Zealand

15. NON-TIME TRAVEL

My father was brought up in the sternest of traditions, and is to this day able to quote Biblical passages of incredible length, word for word, together with several reams of Talmudic commentary on each verse. Since all this is in Hebrew, of which I understand only an occasional word, it does me no good, except for what spiritual edification osmoses inward as a result of hearing the sound of the sonorous syllables of the Language of the Prophets and Patriarchs.

However, all those Biblical and Talmudic passages have served to inculcate in my father a lofty code of virtue which he has tried for many years (with mixed results) to pass on to me. One of the fruits of that code, for instance, is my father's complete inability to make use of strong language. In fact, all I have ever heard him say, under even the most extreme provocation, is a phrase which, being translated, means, literally, "Eighteen black years!"

I believe that this represents a wish that the person or object at whom this phrase is aimed suffer eighteen consecutive years of misfortune, but my father refuses to confirm this, considering it an unfit subject for discussion. And when I ask him the significance of "eighteen" and suggest that "seventeen" might be sufficient, he turns away in sorrow, convinced that I am hopelessly sunk in frivolity.

The saddest part of the matter, alas, is that this inconvenient habit of his of speaking without colorful phrases, is something he has indeed managed to pass on to me. I consider even "eighteen black years" to be a rather harsh and unwarranted remark, and, when strongly moved, I usually give vent to an "Oh, dear me!" or an "Oh, goodness gracious!" I may even, in transports of fury, go so far as a "Good Heavens!"

This has had a serious effect on me, aside from the fact that I am occasionally the recipient of a dubious glance or two. When someone makes a remark that shows him to be particularly ignorant of some very simple aspect of science,* a person other than myself could respond with a vile word or two and, unburdening his soul in this manner, pass on to other things. I cannot. Helpless to relieve my feelings with an expletive, I am forced to say, "Well, no, that's not quite right. Here, let me try to explain . . ."

And thus my way of life has been forced upon me.

I'll give you an example. Occasionally I have been on the scene when an individual has discovered that in crossing the Pacific Ocean from Tokyo to San Francisco, there comes a place where you "go backwards in time one day." A look of heavy concentration may come over this person and then the grinding gears produce an awe-inspiring thought:

"Listen," he says, "if you keep on going around the Earth west to east time after time after time, you go backward one day each time and if you go fast enough you can keep from growing older and live forever."

I then search for the proper remark and failing to find it, I am forced to say, "Well, no, that's not quite right. Here, let me try to explain . . ."

We can begin by making things very simple. Let us suppose we have frozen an instant of time. The Earth has stopped in mid-spin at just the moment when the Sun is crossing the meridian over your head so that it is exactly noon at the point

* A "simple aspect of science" may be defined as one which, through good fortune, I happen to understand.

at which you are standing. Furthermore, the day of the week is (pardon me, while I toss my seven-sided coin) Tuesday.

Very well, then, it's noon on Tuesday where you're standing and for our purposes here, it doesn't matter where that point is. Call it Home.

Since we've frozen an instant of time and the Earth is standing still, it is going to be noon on Tuesday indefinitely at Home. You can wander away wherever you want and when you come back the Sun will still be crossing the meridian and it will still be noon on Tuesday. This will give us a chance to experiment at leisure.

Suppose you travel due east from Home. As you travel east along Earth's curved surface, the Sun will seem to move to the west because of the very existence of that curvature. The farther you move east, the further the Sun seems to sink in the west, till finally, if you move far enough eastward, the Sun touches the western horizon.

We associate this apparent westward journey of the Sun from meridian to western horizon with that of a forward-moving time from noon to evening, so we would naturally assume that as we travel east it is getting later in the day.

But we have frozen time. The Sun is in actuality (according to the mythical situation we have arranged) motionless over the meridian of Home. Therefore, the change in time as we travel eastward is an illusion born of our convention that the apparent westward motion of the Sun *must* mean that time is moving forward.

How did that convention arise? Well, let's consider.

The basic and original concept of time is physiological; it is our own sense of duration; our own sense that something is happening and *then* something else is happening and *then* something else is happening and so on.

Of course, our sense of duration is strongly influenced by environment. A period of time at a dull lecture seems to stretch out tremendously. The same period of time (as judged by someone else) spent with a charming girl is alarmingly brief.

You might, of course, take your own sense of duration as an absolute standard of time measurement. If you feel that the lecture endured long and the girl's stay did not, why accept someone else's opinion that the two intervals were about equal in duration?

Alas, you must, if you are outvoted. If there is to be cooperation in the world, and if people are to do anything at all together, they had better drown their own particular senses of duration and choose some average that will suit them all as well as possible. The trick is to choose some change which seems constant in rate over long periods and to use that as a commonly agreed upon measure of time.

The first such steady change available to primitive man, when he began to feel the need of an objective measure of time, was the steady and constant progression, day after day, of the Sun from eastern horizon to western horizon.

Of course, the Sun's apparent motion is not really a fundamental phenomenon. It depends on the accidental fact that the Earth is rotating on its axis at a rate that does not match its revolution about the Sun. Furthermore, this motion is a useful measure of time, only because the Earth's rate of rotation happens to be virtually constant.

Yet it must be pointed out that the apparent progression of the Sun from east to west takes place at a constant rate *only when the observer does not change his position, east and west, on the Earth's surface.* (He can move north and south all he wants provided he ignores the changes introduced by the tilting of the Earth's axis—like a six-month day or night at the poles.)

As soon as an observer moves east or west, he adds to the apparent east-to-west motion of the Sun that results from the Earth's west-to-east rotation, an additional change that is the reflection of his own motion. And since the observer's own motion is bound to be erratic, the progression of the Sun is no longer constant to the moving man and that progression may therefore no longer be a useful measure of time.

To be sure, it is not quite as bad as all that. Ordinary motion, such as walking to the post office, or driving to work, is over distances so short and at a rate so slow compared to the planet's rotational speed, that the irregularity introduced into the Sun's apparent motion is small enough to be ignored. Until a quarter century ago, in fact, motion-induced irregularities were of importance only under highly specialized and exceptional conditions.

Since World War II, however, jet-plane travel has become commonplace. Travel over long distances at great speeds is indulged in. The result is that the apparent motion of the Sun across the sky for such travelers has no reasonable relation whatever to one's sense of duration or to the time measurements conducted by a stay-at-home individual.

Since the traveler tries to adjust his activities to the Sun's position at all times, partly out of habit and partly out of a desire or need to synchronize his activity with those of the natives of the place he has reached, he tries to accept the fact that it is dinner time just because the Sun is on the western horizon. Since his own internal clock knows it *isn't* dinner time there is a conflict that causes the traveler to feel rotten. And so our age gets a new disease, the Jet-set Jitters.

The progression of the Sun is not, of course, the only method we have of telling time. In fact, when it comes to telling time to better than the nearest hour, we've *got* to use something other than the Sun. We use the constant periodic motion of a hairspring in a wristwatch, for instance.

Not only does the wristwatch tell us the time to the second (if it is working well) but it is not significantly affected by our motion, or change in position, even as a result of jet travel. Our wristwatch will measure a time lapse roughly equivalent to our sense of duration whether that time lapse has taken place while we were in our bed at Home, or while we traveled half around the Earth in a jet plane.

And yet do we go by our wristwatch? No, we do not. Synchronization with the activities of the natives which, in turn, are matched to the progression of the Sun, is a matter of overriding concern. If we jet from New York to London, we ignore our correct wristwatch; we change its setting to match the position of the Sun, and it's hello, Jitters, hello.

Indeed, think of how convenient things might be if we lived underground and never saw the Sun. It would be simplicity itself (in principle) to set up a single light-dark alternation for the entire planet, so that it could then be noon everywhere at the same time. We could then travel quickly or slowly through such an underground world, and over distances that were large or small, yet never experience any of the time problems we experience on the Earth's surface.

In other words, then, our time problems on Earth arise entirely out of the fact that we are living on a spinning sphere and have gotten into the habit of matching our behavior to the relative position of ourselves and the Sun. Our problems are a matter of convention only and have nothing to do with time itself as a physical phenomenon.

Nothing we can do on the surface of the Earth does more than play games with convention; nothing we can do affects the steady flow of physical time.

Forget, then, about time travel. That is not involved in the slightest. Forget about time as a physical phenomenon. Think only of the convention of the Sun's apparent movement and let's see how we can handle that convention in such a way as to keep us from becoming involved in contractions and paradoxes.

Let's start again at Home at a frozen instant of time at noon, Tuesday, and travel eastward. Every fifteen degrees we travel will make Sun-based time one hour later (see Chapter 14).

It is therefore 1 P.M. Tuesday at 15° eastward, 2 P.M. Tuesday at 30° eastward, and so on, until we reach 12 P.M.—that is, midnight—when we have traveled 180° eastward and have completed a journey that is exactly halfway around the world on the particular parallel of latitude we are following. (The same holds true for any parallel of latitude, of course. Movement north and south from one parallel of latitude to another, does not affect Sun-based time.)

Back we go Home, where time's freeze means it is still noon on Tuesday. Now we travel due westward. As we travel westward, the Sun seems to move eastward in the sky and if we go far enough westward it will be seen at the eastern horizon. In short, Sun-based time will be earlier and earlier as we go westward.

Again, each 15° stretch that we travel westward makes the Sun-based time one hour earlier. It is 11 A.M. Tuesday at 15° westward; 10 A.M. Tuesday at 30° westward, and so on, until we reach a time of midnight when we travel 180° westward and have completed a journey that is again exactly halfway around the world on the particular parallel of latitude we are following.

This appears delightfully consistent. Whether we travel 180° due east or 180° due west we end up at exactly the same place, the point exactly opposite Home on its parallel of latitude. (If Home is Boston, for instance—42.3° North Latitude, 71.1° West Longitude—then 180° either due east or due west is near the town of Pai-yun-o-po in Inner Mongolia.) And whether we go due east or due west, it turns out to be midnight at that 180° opposite point.

But wait, heave no sigh of relief, for we are in trouble!

Look more closely at the eastern progression from Home. As we travel over 15° intervals, we move to 1 P.M. Tuesday, 2 P.M. Tuesday, 3 P.M. Tuesday until we finally reach, at 180° eastward, the midnight that follows one minute after 11:59 P.M. Tuesday. It is the midnight that forms the boundary between Tuesday and Wednesday. Let's call it: 12 P.M. Tuesday/Wednesday.

If we move westward from Home, however, the progression

is 11 A.M. Tuesday, 10 A.M. Tuesday, 9 A.M. Tuesday, until we finally reach, at 180° westward, the midnight that just precedes by one minute the time of 12:01 A.M. Tuesday. That is the midnight that separates Monday from Tuesday and we can call it: 12 P.M. Monday/Tuesday.

In short, in traveling either east or west we find that it is indeed midnight at the 180° line in either case, but it is a *different midnight* in each case. The westward travel takes us to the 180° line at a time which, apparently, is 24 hours *earlier* than that same 180° line is when reached by eastward travel.

This is a paradox that is caused, let me repeat, not by the nature of time itself, but by the conventions of Sun-based time only. It is a man-made paradox!

The paradox gets worse if we continue our travel past the 180° line. Suppose we have reached the 180° line traveling eastward and find it is 12 P.M. Tuesday/Wednesday and continue traveling eastward another 15°. Judging by the Sun (which is on the other side of the Earth and is not visible, but whose position can be calculated), another hour has been gained and it is now 1 A.M. Wednesday. Another 15° eastward brings us to 2 A.M. Wednesday and so on.

Finally, when we have gone 180° past the 180° line, and have traveled 360° eastward altogether, we find we have made a complete circle and have returned Home. By that time, we calculate the time to be noon on Wednesday. In other words, in traveling 360° eastward (and returning Home), we have passed over twenty-four 15° intervals and considered ourselves to have moved forward in time one hour for each of those intervals, and twenty-four hours (or one full day) forward for the complete circuit. Hence, while we considered it to be noon on Tuesday when we left Home, we considered it noon on Wednesday when we returned Home.

Yet we have been assuming frozen time. The Earth has not moved; the Sun is still where it was.

Next, suppose you had traveled westward instead of eastward.

Now you would have counted one hour earlier at each 15° interval, reaching 12 P.M. Monday/Tuesday at the 180° line and 11 P.M. Monday when you had reached 15° west of it, then 10 P.M. Monday, 9 P.M. Monday until when you reached Home again, you could consider it noon on Monday.

Imagine, then, three men at Home. One stays Home, one travels eastward at a constant speed, and one travels westward at a constant speed. The two travelers return Home at the same moment. The one who has not left Home says: "It is still noon on Tuesday." The one who traveled eastward says, "It is noon on Wednesday." The one who traveled westward says, "It is noon on Monday."*

Furthermore, if our travelers keep on traveling at constant speed in the same direction, they will continue periodically to meet at Home. Each time they meet, the eastward traveler will add a day, the westward traveler will subtract a day, and the stay-at-home will insist on an unchanged day.

The situation would not be altered, in essence, if the travelers went at unequal speeds, or each at varying speeds, just as long as one moved generally eastward and the other generally westward.

You might wonder if there would be a difference if we allowed for the fact that the Earth is rotating, and that time is not actually frozen. No! The rotating Earth would advance time for all three individuals, the stay-at-home and the two travelers, but superimposed on that advancing time which all three would experience equally, there would be a day added for each circle of the earth by the eastward traveler and a day subtracted for each circle of the earth by the westward traveler.

How's that for a paradox? Well, to repeat once more, it is a man-made paradox based on a man-made convention of Sun-based time. To correct it, one need only adjust the convention properly.

* I believe that Edgar Allan Poe wrote a comic farce based on a situation like the one described here.

How is that done?

Suppose we fix the time on any part of the Earth as it would be calculated traveling east or west from Home *by whichever route is shorter*. Continuing to use frozen time, let's leave Home at noon on Tuesday and travel 90° eastward (crossing six 15° sections). If we cross six 15° sections, we move six hours forward and, on arriving at our destination, we find the time to be 6 P.M. Tuesday.

We might also leave Home at noon on Tuesday and reach the same point by traveling 270° westward (eighteen 15° sections). If we then move eighteen hours backward, we find the time to be 6 P.M. Monday at our destination.

In this case, since the 90° eastward trip was shorter than the 270° westward trip, it is the decision of the former that counts. It is 6 P.M. Tuesday, whether you travel eastward or westward. The same sort of decision can be made for any other combinations of east travel versus west travel.

Consider now, that the eastward trip is the shorter for all points up to 180° eastward of Home; the westward trip is the shorter for all points up to 180° westward of home. It is precisely at the 180° line, which is the same whether you travel east or west, that there is a conflict.

If you travel eastward to a point just short of the 180° line you will find it 11:59 P.M. Tuesday. If you travel westward to a point just short of the 180° mark you will find it 12:01 A.M. Tuesday. If, still moving eastward, the eastward traveler now crosses the 180° line, he must suddenly abandon his own calculations and accept those of the westward traveler. Instead of reaching 12:01 A.M. Wednesday as his own calculations would tell him, he finds himself at 12:01 A.M. Tuesday, as the other's calculations would have it. The eastward traveler moves back in time twenty-four hours—a whole day—by crossing the 180° line.

Similarly the westward traveler who crosses the 180° line, while still moving west, must abandon his own calculations for those of the eastward traveler. Instead of finding himself to be at

11:59 P.M. Monday, as his own calculations would have it, he finds it 11:59 P.M. Tuesday as the eastward traveler would insist. The westward traveler, in moving west across the 180° line, moves forward in time twenty-four hours—a whole day.

It is this moving forward or backward, a whole day at a time that, to the casual observer, seems to introduce the possibility of a paradox. A day has been "gained" or it has been "lost." You have grown "a day younger" or "a day older."

Nonsense! That trick about crossing the 180° line is designed to *prevent* a paradox—the very paradox I mentioned earlier in the article, in which eastward travelers move a day forward each time they circle the Earth, as compared with a motionless observer, and westward travelers move a day backward.

With the modified convention of the 180° line, the situation is as follows: The eastward traveler moves 1 hour forward with each 15° he covers, and has moved 24 hours forward, little by little, by the time he has covered 360° and returned Home. *But* he has moved 24 hours backward, all at once, the instant he crossed the 180° line and that neatly canceled the gradual forward change of the eastward progression. Having moved forward 24 hours little by little and 24 hours backward all at once, he returns Home with no change in time and finds it is still noon on Tuesday as the stay-at-home insists.

Similarly the westward traveler moves 1 hour backward for each 15° he covers, moving 24 hours backward when he has covered 360° and returned Home. *But* he has moved 24 hours forward, all at once, the instant he crossed the 180° line and that change is canceled. He, too, agrees it is noon on Tuesday.

In fact, no matter how many times the travelers circle the Earth, and no matter what their direction of travel, no paradox of time measurement will exist as long as the 24-hour jump exists at the 180° line. Nor is this altered in a steadily rotating Earth where time is not frozen. Without the jump at the 180° line, the paradox *would* exist, and jet-age travel would become a jungle of confusion.

But where should the 180° line be? Home is where your heart is and for every different Home there is a different 180° line and my Home and my 180° line is just as good as yours, aren't they?

Yes, it is, but if the same 180° line isn't adopted for everybody, then everything tumbles into confusion anyway.

As it happens, the nineteenth century saw an international agreement on the subject of longitude. In 1884 an international conference was held in Washington to decide on a universally-agreed upon Prime Meridian.

Since Great Britain was the dominant maritime power of the time, it seemed logical to set the 0° longitude mark on the meridian passing through the Greenwich Observatory in London. This is the "Greenwich meridian."

This international agreement deals only with the convention for locating objects on the surface of the Earth. It does *not* deal with time measurements and no official international agreement has been reached there.

Nevertheless, it is unofficially accepted that the time based on the Sun's position at Greenwich (or "Greenwich time") is *the* time. Undoubtedly, when we set up our space stations and our colonies under the Moon's surface—all under conditions where the position of the Sun will mean nothing—it will be Greenwich time that will be used.

Why not, therefore, set our standard as noon on Tuesday at Greenwich, and choose as our 180° line the 180° line as calculated from Greenwich? Since Greenwich is at 0° Longitude (neither east nor west) by definition, the 180° line associated with it happens to be the one that is marked 180° Longitude (neither east nor west) on any map or globe of the Earth.

It is at the line of 180° Longitude, then, that one moves a day backward by crossing it traveling eastward, and moves a day forward by crossing it traveling westward.

As it happens, this—through sheer accident—is the most convenient arrangement possible. Greenwich Observatory was chosen as the site for the Prime Meridian for reasons that had nothing to do with time measurement, yet its 180° line travels north-south right through the middle of the Pacific Ocean, at precisely the point where a day change can be made with the least possible inconvenience.

It would be unthinkable, for instance, to have the 180° line pass through the middle of the United States, or the middle of the Soviet Union and expect people of part of a nation to be operating one day behind or ahead of the people of the other part. As it is the line of 180° Longitude crosses over ocean water through almost its entire length in places that are as far removed from the major land masses as possible. Imagine just that line happening to be opposite London!

To be sure, 180° Longitude does cut across the eastern tip of Siberia and make its way through some island chains. The line along which a sudden twenty-four-hour change takes place is therefore not precisely along the 180° Longitude line throughout its stretch. The accepted line of change bends east and west as much as three to five hundred miles in places in order to place the tip of Siberia with the rest of the Soviet Union on one side of the line and the westmost Aleutian Islands with the rest of the United States on the other side of the line. South of the equator there is an eastern bulge to allow certain islands to be on the same side of the line as Australia and New Zealand.

This somewhat irregular line is the "International Date Line"—which is made use of internationally, even though it has never been the subject of an official international agreement!

And there you are! No amount of crossing the date line can in any possible way involve you in paradoxes, and certainly it can never—by any conceivable stretch of the imagination—involve you in time-travel.

Please say you see it now, for if you don't, I am all out of explanation, and I still don't have any exclamatory remark to fall back upon.

16. TWELVE POINT THREE SIX NINE

Once in junior high school, my English teacher gave the class the assignment of reading and pondering Leigh Hunt's poem "Abou ben Adhem." Perhaps you remember it.

Abou ben Adhem awoke one night from a deep dream of peace and found an angel making a list of the names of those who loved God. Ben Adhem naturally wanted to know if he was included and was told he wasn't. Humbly he asked to be included as one who loved his fellow men, at least.

The next night the angel reappeared "And show'd the names whom love of God had bless'd/And lo! Ben Adhem's name led all the rest."

I knew the poem and had a pretty good notion as to the course of the class discussion planned for the next day by the teacher. There would be little homilies about how to love God meant to love mankind and vice versa. I agreed with that, but thought it would be rather dull to spend time on so self-evident a proposition. Could not some alternate meaning be wrenched out of the miserably unsubtle poem? I could find none.

The next day, our English teacher, with a kindly smile, asked, "Now, class, who will volunteer to tell me why Abou ben Adhem's name led all the rest?"

Blinding inspiration struck me. I raised my hand violently and when the teacher nodded at me, I said, with a beatific smile, "Alphabetical order, sir!"

I didn't really expect him to be grateful for this new light I was shedding on Leigh Hunt's poem, so I wasn't surprised when he pointed his thumb quietly at the door. I left (knowing the way, for I had been ejected for obstreperous behavior on several previous occasions) and the class discussion went on without me.

But, as I discovered afterward, Abou ben Adhem had been effectively punctured and the teacher had gone on to discuss other matters, so I suppose I won out.

If I get weary of the lack of subtlety in "Abou ben Adhem" you can imagine how desperate I get at those who maintain the entire Universe to be equally unsubtle.

Naturally I get most desperate when the unsubtlety is of a sort to which I feel myself to be (in secret) deeply attracted. For instance, there are those who, having noted some simple and hackneyed relationships between numbers or between geometrical figures, promptly suppose that the structure of the Universe is designed merely to show off those relationships. (And, to my self-disgust, I always find this sort of thing interesting.)

Mystics have been guilty of such simple-mindedness, I am sure, in every society complicated enough to have invented arithmetic, but the best early examples known today are to be found among the Greeks.

For instance, Pythagoras of Samos, about 525 B.C., plucked taut strings and listened to the notes that were produced. He observed that pleasant-sounding combinations of notes were heard when strings were of lengths that bore a simple arithmetical ratio to one other: 1 to 2 or 3 to 4 to 5 (see Chapter 10). It was that, perhaps, which led him and his followers to believe that the physical world was governed by numerical relationships, and simple numerical relationships at that.

It is true, of course, that numerical relationships are of importance in the Universe, but they are not always simple by any means. For instance, a fact of apparently fundamental importance is the ratio of the mass of the proton to the electron—which is 1836.11. Why 1836.11? No one knows.

But we can't blame the Pythagoreans for their lack of knowledge of modern physics. Let us rather consider with astonishment a pupil of Pythagoras by the name of Philolaus of Tarentum. As far as we know, he was the first man in history (about 480 B.C.) to suggest that the Earth moved through space.

Let's try to trace his reasoning. As the Greeks could see, the starry heavens revolved about the Earth. However, seven particular heavenly objects—the Sun, the Moon, Mercury, Venus, Mars, Jupiter, and Saturn—moved independently of the fixed stars and of each other. One might suppose, therefore, that there were eight concentric (and transparent) spheres in the heaven, revolving about the Earth. The innermost contained the Moon affixed to itself, the next Mercury, then Venus, then the Sun, then Mars, Jupiter, Saturn. The eighth and outermost contained the host of stars.

Philolaus was not content with this arrangement. He suggested that the eight spheres did not move about the Earth but about some "central fire." This central fire was invisible, but its reflection could be seen as the Sun. Furthermore, the Earth itself was also fixed in a sphere that revolved about the central fire. And, in addition, there was still *another* body, the "counter-Earth," which we never saw because it stayed always on the side of the Sun opposite ourselves, and that counter-Earth was in still another sphere that revolved about the central fire.

So a total of ten revolving spheres are allowed for in Philolaus' system: the eight ordinary ones, plus a ninth for the Earth, and a tenth for the counter-Earth.

However did Philolaus arrive at that? To be sure, two centuries after his time, Aristarchus of Samos also suggested the Earth moved—but he insisted it moved around the Sun. This was considered absurd at the time, but at least Aristarchus made use of bodies perceptible to the senses. Why did Philolaus invent an invisible central fire and an invisible counter-Earth?

The probable answer rests with the *number* of spheres. If

the Earth revolved about the Sun, you would have to add a sphere for the Earth, but subtract one for the now stationary Sun and the total would still be eight. If you kept both Earth and Sun moving about an invisible center and added a counter-Earth, you would have ten.

And why ten spheres? Well, the Pythagoreans thought ten was a particularly satisfactory number because $1+2+3+4=10$, something which lent itself to involved reasoning that ended in ten as a perfect number. If, then, we argue that the Universe has to be perfect and that its notion of perfection had to agree with that of the Pythagoreans, and if it were further granted that the Universe had no reason for existence but to exhibit that perfection—then the total number of spheres has to be ten (even though two of the spheres have to be kept secret for some arcane reason).

Unfortunately the trouble with all such irrefutable arguments based on the mystical properties of numbers is that no two people can ever quite bring themselves to believe in the same mystique. The Pythagorean notion went out of the window and astronomers contented themselves with eight spheres. Indeed, since the starry sphere was dismissed as mere background, the magic number became seven.

Arguments concerning the structure of the Universe, based on simple arithmetic (and worse) did not die out with the Greeks, by any means.

In 1610 Galileo, using the telescope, discovered that Jupiter had four lesser bodies circling it. This meant that there were eleven bodies (excluding the fixed stars themselves) that circled the Earth according to the old Greek system—or eleven bodies circling the Sun, according to the new-fangled Copernican system.

Great was the opposition to this new discovery, and the arguments against it by one adversary will live forever in the history of human folly.

It was not necessary, explained the learned scholar, to look through the telescope. The new bodies could not be there, since there could only be seven bodies circling the Earth (or Sun) and no more. If the additional bodies were seen, it had to be because of a defect in the telescope, because the new bodies *could not* be there.

And how could one be sure they could not be there? Easy! As there are seven openings in the head—two eyes, two ears, two nostrils, and a mouth—so there must be seven planetary bodies in the heavens.

Thus, it seemed, it was necessary to so order the entire Universe as to make some sort of permanent record in the heavens as to the number of openings in the human head. It was as though God needed crib notes that would enable him to keep the figure in mind so that he wouldn't create Man with the wrong number of openings. (I'm sorry if that sounds blasphemous, for I don't mean it to be so. The blasphemy is on the part of those men, past and present, who try to make it appear that God is a kindergarten infant, playing with number blocks.)

Such folly dies hard. In fact, it never dies.

Astronomers, having accepted the Copernican notion of bodies circling the Sun rather than the Earth, now recognized two classes of bodies in the Solar system.

There were bodies that revolved directly about the Sun; these were the planets and in 1655, six were recognized—Mercury, Venus, Earth, Mars, Jupiter, and Saturn. Then, there were bodies that revolved not about the Sun directly, but about one of the planets. These were the satellites and there were five of them recognized at the time: our own Moon and the four satellites of Jupiter, which Galileo had discovered (Io, Europa, Ganymede, and Callisto).

But in 1655 the Dutch astronomer Christian Huygens discovered a satellite of Saturn which he named Titan. That meant the Solar system consisted of six planets and six satellites. Huygens was a first-class scientist and a great figure in the history of astronomy and physics, but he wasn't proof against the symmetry of six and six. He announced that the total was complete. No more bodies remained to be found.

Alas, in 1671 the Italian-French astronomer Giovanni D. Cassini discovered another satellite of Saturn and spoiled the symmetry. Huygens lived to see it, too. Indeed, he lived to see Cassini discover three more satellites of Saturn.

Then we have Johann Kepler, who was not content with merely working out the number of heavenly bodies on the basis of simple arithmetic. He went a step further and tried to work out the relationships among the distances of those bodies from the Sun by interconnection with simple geometry.

There are five and only five regular solids (solids with all faces equal and all angles equal—as is true, for instance, of the cube, the most familiar of the five).

Why not reason as follows, then? The regular solids are perfect and so is the Universe. There are just five regular solids and, since there are six planets, there are just five interplanetary gaps.

Kepler therefore attempted to nest the five regular solids in such a way that the six planets moved along the various boundaries in the proper relationship of distances. Kepler spent a lot of time trying to adjust his solids and failed. (The acid test, that makes Kepler a great deal more than a crackpot, is that, having failed, he promptly dropped the notion.)

During the last week of 1966, however, I discovered something about Kepler I had not known before.

I was attending a meeting of the American Association for the Advancement of Science and was listening to papers on the history of astronomy. One particularly interesting paper included the statement that Kepler had felt that there ought to be just 360 days in a year. The Earth was rotating faster than it should have been, which was what made the number of days in the year 365¼. (If the day were 24 hours and 21 minutes long, there would be just 360 days in the year.)

This too-fast rotation of the Earth, in Kepler's view, somehow carried over to the Moon, forcing it to revolve a bit too quickly about the Earth. Obviously the Moon should be revolving about the Earth in just 1/12 of a year; that is, in about 30⅖ days. Instead, it revolved in only about 29½ days.

If the Earth revolved about the Sun in 360 days of 24⅓ hours apiece (naturally, the hours and its subdivisions would be slightly lengthened to make just 24 hours to the slightly longer day), how convenient that would be. After all, 360 is such a pleasant number, being exactly divisible by 2, 3, 4, 5, 6, 8, 9, 10, 12, 15, 18, 20, 24, 30, 36, 40, 45, 60, 72, 90, 120, and 180. No other number approximating its size is evenly divisible in so many different ways.

And if each lunar month were equal to 30 days of a little over 24 hours each, there would be exactly 12 lunar months in a year. The number 12 is evenly divisible by 2, 3, 4, and 6; and 30 by 2, 3, 5, 6, 10, and 15.

Nor is it just a matter of tricks of numbers. With 30 days to the lunar month and 12 lunar months to the year, a beautifully simple calendar could be devised.

Instead, what do we have? About 29½ days to a lunar month, about 365¼ days to a year, and about 12⅜ lunar months to the year. And the result of this farrago of fractions? Nearly five thousand years of fiddling with calendars that has ended with one that is *still* inconvenient.

My thoughts might have ended there, but the lecturer at the AAAS meeting gave the number of lunar months in the year in decimal form rather than fractions. He said, "Instead of 12 lunar months to a year, there are 12.369."*

My eyebrows raised in astonishment at once. Indeed? Are there really 12.369 lunar months in a year? My mind began fitting notions together and at the conclusion of the lecture I raised my hand to ask a question. I wanted to know if Kepler had tried to draw a certain simple deduction from that

* Actually, this is wrong, I think. According to the best figures I can find, the number of lunar months in a year is closer to 12.368. It is 12.36827, to be exact. But let's not spoil my chapter.

figure. No, said the lecturer, it sounds like something Kepler might have done, but he didn't.

Excellent! Excellent! That left me free to indulge in a little mysticism of my own. After all, every one knows I am in love with figures, and I could easily design the Universe in order to show off first-grade arithmetic. What's more, I happen to be interested in the Bible, so why not show that the design of the Universe is connected with certain elementary statistics involving the Bible?

(I am not without precedent here. Isaac Newton was an indefatigable Biblical student who produced nothing worthy of note; and the Scottish mathematician John Napier, who first worked out logarithms, also worked out a completely worthless system for interpreting the Book of Revelation.)

Let me, therefore, go along with Kepler. Let us suppose that the whole purpose of the rate of Earth's rotation about its axis, the Moon's revolution about the Earth, and the revolution of the Earth/Moon system about the Sun, is to present mankind with pretty numbers and a symmetrical calendar.

What, then, went wrong? Surely God knew what he was doing and would not make a careless mistake. If the year were more than 360 days long there would have to be a reason for it; an exact reason. The error would be no error but would be something designed to instruct mankind in the simple-minded manner that mystics seem to like to consider characteristic of God.

There are 365¼ days in a year so that the excess over 360 (the "right" number) is 5¼ or, in decimal form, 5.25. You must admit now that 5.25 is an interesting number since 25 is the square of 5.

Let's reason like a mystic. Can 5.25 be a coincidence? Of course not. It must have meaning and that meaning must be in the Bible. (After all, God is the center about which the Bible revolves as the Sun is the center about which the Earth revolves. What is more natural than to find in the revolving Bible the reasons for the details of the revolving Earth.)

The Old Testament, according to tradition, is divided into three parts: the Law, the Prophets, and the Writings. All are holy and inspired, but the Law is the most sacred portion and that is made up of the first five books of the Bible: Genesis, Exodus, Leviticus, Numbers, and Deuteronomy.

Why, then, are there five days beyond the "proper" 360? Surely in order to mark the five books of the Law in the very motions of the Earth. And why the extra quarter day beyond the five? Why, to make the excess not merely 5 but 5.25. By squaring the 5 and emphasizing it in that fashion, the Law is demonstrated to be not only holy, but particularly holy.

Of course, there is a catch. The length of the year is not really precisely 365.25 days. It is a bit short of that, and is 365.2422 days long. (To be even more precise it is 365.242197 days long, but 365.2422 is close enough, surely.)

Does that mean that the whole scheme falls to the ground? If you think so, you don't know how the mind of a mystic works. The Bible is so large and complex a book that almost any conceivable number can be made to have a Biblical significance. The only limit is the ingenuity of the human mind.

Let's, for instance, take a look at 365.2422. The excess over the "proper" 360 is 5.2422. The figures to the right of the decimal point can be broken up into 24 and 22 and the average is 23. What, then, is the significance of the 23?

We have settled that the 5 represents the five books of the Law. That leaves the Prophets and the Writings. How many books are contained in those? The answer is 34.*

That doesn't seem to get us anywhere—but wait. Twelve of the books are relatively short prophetic works: Hosea, Joel, Amos, Obadiah, Jonah, Micah, Nahum, Habakkuk, Zephaniah, Haggai, Zechariah, and Malachi. For convenience, in ancient

* At least according to Jews and Protestants. The Roman Catholic version of the Bible includes eight additional books considered apocryphal by Jews and Protestants.

times, these were often included in a single roll which was referred to as the Book of the Twelve.

Thus, in the apocryphal book of Ecclesiasticus (accepted as canonical by the Catholics) the author—writing about 180 B.C. —lists the great men of Biblical history. After mentioning the major prophets individually, he lumps the minor prophets together:

> Ecclesiasticus 49:10. *And of the twelve prophets let the memorial be blessed . . .*

Well, then, if the twelve minor prophets be included as a single book—as there is ample precedent for doing—how many books are there in the Prophets and Writings together by the Jewish/Protestant count? Why, 23.

We can therefore say that of the number of days in the year (365.2422), 360 days represent the "correct" figure, 5 days represent the Law, and 0.2422 represent the Prophets and the Writings. The days of the year thus become a memorial to the Old Testament.

That takes us to the number of lunar months in the year, which is 12.369, the number that first attracted my attention. If the days in the year represent the Old Testament, then surely the lunar months in the year must represent the New Testament. Any mystic will tell you that this is self-evident.

Well, then, what can we say would be a central difference between the Old Testament and the New Testament? We might try this: In the Old Testament, God is treated as a single entity while in the New Testament, He is revealed as a Trinity. Consequently if this is so, and if the number of lunar months in a year represents the New Testament, that number should somehow be related to the number 3.

And if we look at 12.369, we see that it is neatly divisible by 3. Hurrah! We are on the right track, as any fool can plainly see (provided he *is* a fool, of course).

Let us, then, divide 12.369 by 3, and we come out with 4.123. Surely that is a highly significant number, consisting, as it does, of the first four integers.

And what connection do the first four integers have with the New Testament? Why the answer is obvious and springs to the mind at once.

The four gospels, of course! The four separate biographies of Jesus by Matthew, Mark, Luke, and John.

It so happens that Gospels 1, 2, and 3—Matthew, Mark, and Luke—give essentially the same view of Jesus. Many of the incidents found in one are found in the others and the general trend of events is virtually identical in all. These are the "synoptic Gospels," the word "synoptic" meaning "with one eye." Gospels 1, 2, and 3 all see Jesus with the same eye, so to speak.

Gospel 4, that of John, is quite different from the other three; differing, in fact, on almost every point, even quite basic ones.

Therefore, if we are going to have the number of lunar months in the year signify the Gospels, would it not be right to group 1, 2, and 3 together and keep 4 separate? And is this not precisely what is done in a number like 4.123?

If you had doubts before, would you not admit we were on the right track now?

We can say then that of the number of lunar months in a year, 12.369, the 12 represents the Gospel of John (4 times 3, for the Trinity) and the 0.369 represent the Synoptic Gospels (123 times 3).

But why is the Fourth Gospel first? Why is a third of the number of lunar months in a year 4.123, rather than 123.4?

This is a good and legitimate question and I have an answer. If the central fact of the New Testament is the Trinity, we must ask how the matter of the Trinity is handled in the various Gospels.

The first evidence of the existence of all three aspects of God together is at the time of Jesus' baptism by John the Baptist (who, of course, is *not* the John who wrote the Fourth Gospel).

In Mark, the oldest of the Gospels, the incident at the baptism is described as follows:

> Mark 1:10. *And . . . he* [Jesus] *saw the heavens opened, and the Spirit like a dove descending upon him:*
> Mark 1:11. *And there came a voice from heaven, saying, Thou art my beloved Son, in whom I am well pleased.*

Here Father, Son, and Holy Spirit are all present at once. Nothing in this account, however, would make us necessarily think that this manifestation was apparent to anyone outside the Trinity. There is nothing to make us suppose, for instance, (if Mark only is considered) that John the Baptist, who was present at that moment, was also aware of the descent of the Spirit, or heard the voice from heaven.

Similar accounts are given in Matthew 3:16–17, and in Luke 3:22. Neither in Matthew nor in Luke is it stated that anyone outside the Trinity was aware of what was happening.

In John's Gospel, however, the Fourth, the account of the descent of the Spirit is placed in the mouth of John the Baptist.

> John 1:32. *And John bare record, saying, I saw the Spirit descending from heaven like a dove, and it abode upon him.*

Since, in Gospel 4, the first manifestation of the Trinity is described as clearly apparent to man, something that is not so in Gospels 1, 2, and 3, then obviously the number *ought* to be 4.123, rather than 123.4.

What more can anyone want?

Now let me emphasize something I hope has been quite apparent to everyone. I am merely playing with numbers. What I have presented here in connection with the days and months in the year has been made up out of my head, and I am no more serious about it than I was, once long ago, about the alphabeticity of Abou ben Adhem.

And yet I would not be in the least surprised to find that

some people were tempted to think there was something to all this nonsense. They might wonder if I had accidentally stumbled on a great truth without knowing it, even while I was imagining myself to be doing nothing more than playing silly games.

And I suppose that some people (maybe even the same people) would say: "Hey, I'll bet Abou ben Adhem's name led all the rest because the list *was* in alphabetical order."

PART III

AND I

17. PORTRAIT OF THE WRITER AS A BOY

I'm not at the Beatle level as far as getting fan mail is concerned, but I do get some, and almost all of it is very gratifying, I'm glad to say.

Some items, however, plunge me into frustration, for while I am anxious to accommodate those who take the trouble to write me, such accommodation is sometimes impossible. There is the case of the youngster, for instance, who writes that he is engaged in a science project on the Solar system, so would I please send him a copy of everything I have ever written on the Solar system plus any other material I might have.

Invariably this letter concludes with a hasty P.S., "Please answer at once as the project must be completed by the 15th." Just as invariably, I receive the letter (forwarded by way of a publisher) on the 16th.

It's a slow week in the school term when several letters like that don't arrive.

My frustration grows worse when accommodation is not actually impossible but merely demands more of my industry than I am willing to give. For instance, there seems to be an increasing number of teen-agers who, for their term papers in English Literature, are choosing to write critical reviews of the writings of your humble servant (well, of *me*, for those of you who don't recognize me by that description).

That's fine, and delightful for the ego, but what do I do

when I am instantly bombarded by dozens of questions like: What got you interested in writing? What writers most influence you? What are your favorite stories? What do you consider the importance of science fiction to society?

I have to write each eager young scholar that I cannot answer such letters in proper detail because if I did there would be no time left to do any other writing and future eager young scholars would suffer a dearth of new material to work with.

It has occurred to me, however, that in view of the fact that I can get my answers printed in wholesale lots, I might as well devote the final chapter in this book to the answering of a few of these questions. Of course, it pains my modest and self-effacing nature to talk about myself, but I think I can manage it.

1. *What got you started writing, Dr. Asimov?*

The answer to that, I'm afraid, must be lost in the dim mists of antiquity. At least, as far back as I remember, I was telling myself stories.

I can pinpoint quite accurately, however, the moment at which I first began to think of myself as a "writer." It came about in the fall of 1931, when I was eleven and beginning the ninth grade.

At the time I was an avid science fiction reader as a result of events I will describe later in the article. I was also earnest in my devotion to the "series books" of adventures built around a fixed set of youthful characters.

There was one serious catch to the devoteeship, unfortunately; it lacked much of an object. The public library didn't have copies of *The Rover Boys, Tom Swift, The Darewell Chums, Poppy Ott*, and the others. I lacked money to purchase any. My friends had few copies they were willing to lend me, particularly since if my father found them in my possession he would confiscate them. (My father had high standards of literature.) Consequently only two or three such books ever passed under my avid eyes and I read them and reread them (in secret) with dogged persistence.

And then, one golden day, it occurred to me that I could repair the dreadful lack of reading matter by writing my own books. I was always constructing stories, so why not bend that construction into a specific imitation of a series book, and place it on paper?

A nickel copybook (that is what they cost those days) I could afford; a pen I had—and what more did I need? Only time. So that evening I sat in the corner of the kitchen and began a tale which I entitled "The Greenville Chums in College."

I wrote a chapter and a half in that first flush of ardor. The setting was a small-town college, and I leave it to you to estimate how much knowledge an eleven-year-old product of the Brooklyn slums could have of either small towns or colleges, but no one had yet told me that I should write only of that which I knew. (For that matter, I never did succeed in learning that elementary rule of writer's conduct, so that eventually I wrote long novels concerning the far reaches of the Galaxy, even though I have no direct experience with those regions either.)

With the chapter and a half done, I felt in a curiously exalted state. I found myself caught in my first attack of that serious disease I call Writer's Folly, the most severe symptom of which is an irrepressible desire to tell someone all about the great novel you're writing.

I buttonholed the first ninth-grade friend I met the next day during the lunch period. "Listen to a story I'm writing," I said.

"What?" he said, turning to me, in a lackluster manner.

"Listen," I said urgently, and began to tell him the story in the very selfsame glorious words I had been putting to paper, for these, naturally, had burned themselves indelibly upon my ringing brain. Slowly his expression gained interest as I spoke, reaching a pitch of almost painful concentration by the time I came to where I had suspended operations and had to stop.

He said, "What comes next?"

"I don't know yet," I said.

He gripped my arm hard. "I get the book first after you're finished reading it, okay? Don't lend it to anyone else!"

"Okay," I said, confused, and wandered off, with tumultuous passions surging through my bosom. He had clearly not heard me say this was a book I was *writing*. He thought I was reading an already written book, a professionally written book, and he found it so exciting he wanted to borrow it.

At that very moment I realized that I was a *writer*. I had, after all, interested a potential reader and I recognized the need for no other qualification. I never doubted my own position as a writer in the years since and when I finally abandoned "The Greenville Chums" after eight chapters or so, it was only to begin something else.

The next important step in the progression came in 1934 when I was completing my junior year in high school. My father, observing my scribblings, and having a European respect for "learning" and for even the suspicion of literary talent, decided that I needed a typewriter. The only trouble was that in those days a typewriter fell into the same class with mink coats and yachts: we couldn't afford one.

How long my father scrounged about, and how many leads he followed, I don't know, but he eventually came upon an ancient upright Underwood No. 5 that worked perfectly and that cost ten dollars.

That wasn't all he did for me, either. He went a giant step further by insisting on the proper use of the machine. He came upon me a few days later, operating the typewriter. Having gazed at me with paternal fondness for a moment, he happened to note that I was hunting down letter after letter and then striking the necessary keys with one stiff forefinger.

He said, "I see people doing the typewriter with all the fingers like a piano."

I said, "I don't know how to do that, Pa."

So he put his hand on the typewriter and said, "All right, then find out how. I catch you once more doing with one finger, I take away the typewriter."

Since I had learned, a long time before, that my father's unreasonableness was exceeded only by his stubbornness, I didn't attempt to argue. I found a young lady who knew how to type and got her to tell me which finger went with which key. Then, since I typed several hours each day, I soon got the hang of it. My typing became first legible and then speedy. Eventually I could crank a hand typewriter at seventy words a minute and, now that I have an electric typewriter, I recently timed myself at ninety words a minute.

I never forgot the lesson, either. My son, having inherited the gene for typing, has, from early childhood, been interested in my machine. Naturally he wasn't allowed to touch it, but when he was twelve I gave him one for himself and, trying to imitate my father's lofty Talmudic tone (I lack the natural dignity of a European patriarch), told him I would take it away if he hunted-and-pecked and showed him where to put his fingers. Now he can type too.

2. *Yes, yes, Dr. Asimov, but what got you started writing SCIENCE FICTION?*

Ah, yes. My father owned a candy store in my youthful days and to that candy store was attached a newsstand and a magazine rack. The magazine rack was filled with the most delectable fiction you could possibly imagine: *The Shadow, Doc Savage, Detective Stories, Argosy*—even today the thought of it all makes me faint with desire.

Yet all of it, from beginning to end, was forbidden by parental ukase. "Thou shalt not read of the fruit of the rack" came the thunder from above and at the age of six I was given a library card and told to make free, instead, with the learned books on the library shelves.

Well, the library was better than nothing, and I worked my way through it with my eyeglasses glinting feverishly. And yet—my eyeglasses bent with unflagging yearning toward the magazine rack.

Came the day in 1929 when a copy of *Science Wonder Stories* appeared on the rack and attracted my attention. I sneaked a copy down when my father was taking his afternoon nap (my kindly mother was always much more permissive) and looked inside. Spaceships, monsters, ray guns—WOW! I put it back and waited for my father to return.

He did. I pointed to the magazine and said, "Papa, would it be all right to read a magazine about science?"

My father stared at it doubtfully. His English was not yet strong, but the cover showed a futuristic airplane that looked very edifying and there was no denying that the word "science" was clearly inscribed on the cover. He said, "All right."

And that is how I became a science fiction reader.

Naturally, as the years passed, and I grew more and more enthusiastic about science fiction, I felt the increasing urge to turn my writing activities to the more imaginative branches of fiction.

After I got my typewriter, and writing began to be less of a purely mechanical problem, I decided to tackle a particularly ambitious project and took to composing an involved fantasy. To save paper, I remember, I wrote single space, both sides, no margins, and, according to my estimate, I wrote sixty thousand words before fagging out.

The fantasy (title forgotten) involved the chaotic battling of a group of seven men against the awful powers of darkness. I followed them through their separations and reunions and sustained them against the hosts of goblins, magicians, and supernatural forces that opposed them.

I thought little of that early effort until last year when I came across Tolkien's *Lord of the Rings* trilogy and finally read it. I realized, to my chagrin, that thirty years ago I had been attempting to forestall Tolkien. Oh, well . . .

By 1936 I was entering my sophomore year in college and I felt I had gained sufficient depth in science to tackle straight science fiction. Consequently I began an interminable novel, whose title and plot escape me now. It too went on for many thousands of words.

It was not until 1937, six years after I had become a writer, that I had a perfectly blinding inspiration. Why novels? Why, for goodness' sake, interminable novels that I inevitably outgrew and abandoned? Why not short stories that I could finish before I tired? What a tribute to my well-known brilliance that this occurred to me after only six years.

No sooner thought than done. In May 1937 I sat down to begin the first short story I ever wrote. It was a science fiction short and was entitled "Cosmic Corkscrew." The thesis was that time was shaped like a helix and that, under certain conditions, it was possible to cut across the coils of the helix. Each coil advanced time about a century, so that one could travel a century into the future, or two centuries, or three, but never, say, 125 years or 263 years into the future or past. I had, in effect, quantized time travel.

The actual plot dealt with a man who traveled a hundred years into the future and found the Earth deserted of all animal life, but showing every trace of recent occupation in peace and security. There was no hint of any reason or explanation for the catastrophe and there was no way he could slide back in time just a few days to find out what had happened.

About the only other thing I can remember about the story is that I casually mentioned the Verrazano Bridge between Brooklyn and Staten Island, only I didn't call it that. I called it the Roosevelt Bridge. Well, you can't be perfect.

I worked away on that story for over a year even though it was only nine thousand words long.

3. *I understand, Dr. Asimov, but how did you first come to PUBLISH a science fiction story?*

Oh!

Well, in writing "Cosmic Corkscrew" I had some dim notion of submitting it for publication. The trouble was, though, that I didn't know how that was done and I lacked the intelligence to ask anyone. So my interest in the story flagged a bit and I think that, but for a purely fortuitous circumstance, it might never have been submitted, or even finished, and that my professional writing career, if it came at all, would have been much delayed.

In those days, you see, I was such an avid science fiction reader that my entire life revolved about the instants of arrival of the various magazines, particularly *Astounding*. Since my father still had a newsstand and magazine rack, I knew the exact day and hour when the magazines might be expected and those days were marked in purple and gold for me. *Astounding*, for instance, arrived on the third Wednesday of each month.

(In fact, until very recently, I still owned the copy of the complete works of Shakespeare that I had used in my 1937 Shakespeare course; a copy that had a row of mysterious numbers marked down the endpaper. Those numbers weren't really mysterious. Each period of that class, while the professor spoke reverently of Shakespeare, I computed the number of hours that must elapse before the arrival of the next science fiction magazine and wrote that number down.)

Then came April 1938 and I waited for the May issue of *Astounding* with an almost maniacal frenzy. A new sequel by Jack Williamson ("The Legion of Time") was to begin and I was an ardent Jack Williamson fan.

Came April 20 and I rushed home on wings. "Where's *Astounding,* Pa?" I asked.

"It didn't come," said my father, too busy with his chores to grasp the magnitude of the blow he had leveled at the very core of my being.

I was stunned. It was Wednesday. The third Wednesday.

"I'll be back," I said hastily, and set off. I knew every newsstand within a mile of our own (they were competitors!) and there wasn't one I missed. I came back hours later, with a drawn, wild countenance that greatly alarmed my mother (who is four feet ten, was already prematurely gray even then, and who has always had enough alarm potential to fill someone with three times her cubic volume).

Astounding was nowhere to be had!

The next day, no *Astounding;* nor the next. I went through my school work with dull detachment; I performed my share of the labor in the store with an aching heart, for always I had to stare at that mocking wall of magazines, minus *Astounding*.

I had only one hope. Some jerk at Street and Smith had miscounted Wednesdays! Surely that was it! Surely *Astounding* would come out on April 27, the fourth Wednesday.

It didn't!

I had to face the ultimate. I had enough experience at the magazine rack to know that magazines sometimes ceased publication. If that had happened to *Astounding*, my own life was over. I would have to join the Foreign Legion to forget. But first I had to know for sure.

Desperation nerved me to wild expedients. I looked up Street and Smith in the phone book and taking a nickel from the cash register, I called them up. "Where is the May *Astounding?*" I asked faintly.

The young lady at the other end informed me with carefree idiocy that publication date had been changed from third Wednesday to fourth Friday and the magazine would be out on April 29. And so it was.

To this day I cannot condone the criminal indifference of the higher echelons at Street and Smith. How dared they make such a change in publication date without informing the readers? Vile executives! Heaven knows how many youngsters died during that unexpected nine-day drought.

That incident affected my writing career in two ways. In the first place, the period during which I feared that *Astounding* had died scarred me permanently. It was from then on that I grew aware of mortality. I realized that I must not delay finishing my short story; I was not immortal. So I got to work and finished.

Second, I had *called* Street and Smith. The organization actually existed—not in some strange Galaxy but a mere half hour by subway from my home. At that organization were real people, ordinary human beings, who *talked* to me. Why not simply go there then (the offices were at 79 Seventh Avenue in those days) and hand in my story?

In June 1938 I did just that. I walked up to the reception desk and in choked tones managed to whisper a request to see Mr. John W. Campbell, Jr. (the new editor of *Astounding*) in order that I might deliver a manuscript.

The receptionist called Mr. Campbell and I closed my eyes and waited for the decapitating blow to fall. Instead she said briskly, "Mr. Campbell will see you!"

I was directed through huge rooms filled with bales of paper and piles of magazines (including the next [!!!!] issue of *Astounding*). I shall carry the odor of the place with me all my life. Even today, the smell of old pulp magazines will make me an eighteen-year-old again.

John Campbell spoke to me for an hour, put me at ease, acted delighted at my having submitted a story. John is still editor of *Astounding* (under its new name of *Analog*) and I have seen John many times since then. Naturally, he treated me with every consideration in later years when he was anxious to have stories from me; but he treated me with *just as much consideration* when I was a frightened eighteen-year-old whom he had never heard of.

If you expect the story to end with an account of how John accepted the very first story I submitted to him and that I was instantly recognized as a science fiction great, forget it. That may have happened to A. E. van Vogt and to Robert A. Heinlein, but not to me. John read the story that evening and mailed it back the next day. Accompanying it was a two-page letter, pinpointing my errors and containing much gentle encouragement.

It is impossible to describe the pleasantness of a rejection like that. After that I wrote science fiction stories at the rate of one or more a month and brought each one in to John Campbell. Each time I came, I was invited in; each time there was a long friendly talk; each time he rejected the story with a helpful letter; each time I was all the more encouraged.

As a writer, I owe John Campbell everything; and I know for a fact that I am not the only science fiction writer who does.

Each story that John returned went next to the two other science fiction magazines that then existed: *Amazing Stories* and *Thrilling Wonder Stories*. The rejections piled up and in the space of four months I had piled up half a dozen.

It didn't faze me, for in addition to John Campbell's goodness to me, my father committed an act of faith that in turn committed me irrevocably to pushing forward.

The rejections bothered my father not at all. He valued my ambition and drive and his values were untarnished by consideration of either fame or financial success. That I *try* was all he required of me.

My learned stories, he felt, were deserving of more than an old relic of an Underwood upright. Somehow, therefore, he managed to raise $65 with which to buy me a *brand-new* Smith-Corona portable, a typewriter I still own to this day.

With that gleaming portable lying before me, it would have taken a much more unfilial person than myself to avoid making the resolution to earn back that money for my father if it took me ten years.

It didn't take ten years after the purchase, thank goodness. It took more like ten weeks.

In October 1938 there came an envelope from *Amazing Stories* and in it was a check for $64. It was my very first professional earning and it paid off the typewriter.

The envelope also contained a very kind letter from Ray Palmer, then editor of *Amazing*, telling me how much he liked my story. I was in no position to frame the check, so I framed the letter of acceptance.

The story I sold was "Marooned Off Vesta." It was the third short story I had written and, I might add, I had written it on my old relic.* It was published in the March 1939 issue of *Amazing* which reached the stands in January, just a couple of weeks after my nineteenth birthday. With that, I became a published writer.

* In 1939 I sold the second short story I had ever written—"The Callistan Menace"—but I never sold the first one.

Meanwhile, I kept up the monthly bombardment of John Campbell and finally my ninth story ("Trends") was accepted by him. It appeared in the July 1939 issue of *Astounding Science Fiction,* the same issue which contained A. E. van Vogt's first story, "Black Destroyer," and the issue before the one which contained Robert A. Heinlein's first story, "Life-Line."

4. *And whatever happened to the stories you wrote before you were published?*

Gone, gone, all gone!

In fact, in my life, I have written six short stories, I think, that were never published—all of them between 1938 and 1940. Not one of them remains. I don't know where they went; in the vicissitudes of life they vanished.

I don't particularly regret these six stories. They were not too different in style from those earliest stories of mine that *were* published.

However, those interminable novels I wrote in the early 1930s—those I do miss.

In particular I would give a large sum to have that nickel copybook again; the one in which I wrote the eight chapters of "The Greenville Chums in College."

I love being a writer; I always have loved being a writer; and I would very greatly value the story that made me realize I was a writer.

But alas, longing will not bring back that which is gone!